Extra Practice 1.1

Name _____

In Exercises 1–8, describe the pattern. Then list the next 3 numbers.

1. 2, 6, 10, 14, ?, ?, ?

2. 99, 88, 77, 66, ?, ?, ?

3. 15625, 3125, 625, 125, ?, ?, ?

4. 2, 10, 50, 250, ?, ?, ?

5. $\frac{2}{3}$, $\frac{4}{3}$, $\frac{8}{3}$, $\frac{16}{3}$, ?, ?, ?

6. 3, $\frac{9}{2}$, 6, $\frac{15}{2}$, ?, ?, ?

7. 2, $\frac{3}{2}$, $\frac{4}{3}$, $\frac{5}{4}$, ?, ?, ?

8. 5, 10, 30, 120, ?, ?, ?

In Exercises 9–12, describe the pattern. Then list the next 3 letters.

9. D, H, L, ?, ?, ?

10. C, F, I, ?, ?, ?

11. Z, X, V, ?, ?, ?

12. B, D, F, H, ?, ?, ?

In Exercises 13 and 14, write the first 6 numbers in the sequence.

13. The first number is 60. Each succeeding number is 6 less than the preceding number.

14. The first number is 2 and the second number is 3. Each succeeding number is the sum of the two preceding numbers.

In Exercises 15 and 16, draw the next 3 figures in the pattern.

15.

16.

17. The high and low temperatures recorded for a certain January day are 82°F in Tempe, Arizona and 12°F in Duluth, Minnesota, respectively. Explain what the numbers represent.

18. You and a friend both take a math examination. You score a 98 out of 100 points and your friend scores 96 out of 100 points. Who scored better? Explain.

19. You and your family are traveling to the beach for a vacation. You and your family fly in an airliner at an average speed of 375 mph. A friend of yours and her family are traveling to the same beach. They are driving at an average speed of 55 mph. Who gets to the beach first? Explain.

20. In Super Bowl XXVIII, the Dallas Cowboys defeated the Buffalo Bills by a score of 30–13. Explain what the numbers represent.

In Exercises 1–4, write a verbal description of the number sentence.

1. $21 \div 3 = 7$ **2.** $14 + 5 = 19$ **3.** $42 \cdot 3 = 126$ **4.** $133 - 17 = 116$

In Exercises 5–16, find the sum or difference.

5. $52 + 126$ **6.** $312 - 256$ **7.** $783 + 212$ **8.** $85.2 - 42.6$

9. $312.42 - 218.02$ **10.** $0.247 - 0.002$ **11.** $4.05 + 0.02$ **12.** $2.45 + 3.24 + 0.02$

13. $\frac{5}{8} + \frac{2}{8}$ **14.** $\frac{9}{15} - \frac{2}{15}$ **15.** $\frac{2}{8} + \frac{4}{8}$ **16.** $\frac{6}{7} - \frac{5}{7}$

In Exercises 17–28, find the product or quotient.

17. 14×8 **18.** $1400 \div 25$ **19.** $(82)(4.3)$ **20.** $31.56 \div 5.26$

21. $\frac{645}{258}$ **22.** $(3.2)(4.5)$ **23.** 454×31 **24.** $2568/32$

25. 76.25×1.5 **26.** $(4.25)(340)$ **27.** $3335 \div 23$ **28.** $14 \cdot \frac{3}{7}$

In Exercises 29–32, write a number sentence for each model.

29. 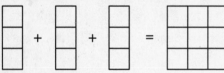   **30.**

31. 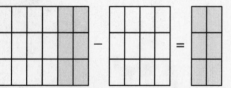   **32.**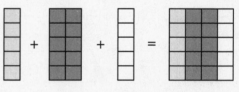

In Exercises 33–35, use the following information:
The top five daily newspapers in the United States,
by circulation in 1991, were The Wall Street Journal,
USA Today, Los Angeles Times, New York Times, and
Washington Post. (Source: The University Almanac)

33. How many more Wall Street Journal newspapers were sold
per day than USA Today newspapers?

34. What was the total circulation of the top five newspapers?

35. If USA Today costs $0.50 per paper, what was the average
daily income for the USA Today?

In Exercises 1 and 2, write a verbal description of the number sentence.

1. $3^4 = 81$

2. $\sqrt{1.69} = 1.3$

In Exercises 3–8, write each expression as a power. Then use a calculator to find the value of the power.

3. 10.5×10.5

4. $7 \times 7 \times 7 \times 7 \times 7$

5. $(1.2)(1.2)(1.2)$

6. $(8.2)(8.2)(8.2)(8.2)$

7. $\frac{2}{5} \cdot \frac{2}{5} \cdot \frac{2}{5} \cdot \frac{2}{5} \cdot \frac{2}{5} \cdot \frac{2}{5}$

8. $\frac{1}{9} \cdot \frac{1}{9} \cdot \frac{1}{9} \cdot \frac{1}{9}$

In Exercises 9–14, find the value of the expression using a calculator. Round your results to two decimal places.

9. $\sqrt{625}$

10. $\sqrt{676}$

11. $\sqrt{243.36}$

12. $\sqrt{596}$

13. $\sqrt{7.5}$

14. $\sqrt{4.25}$

In Exercises 15–20, find the number that is represented by a $\triangle$.

15. $\triangle \cdot \triangle \cdot \triangle = 729$

16. $\triangle \cdot \triangle \cdot \triangle \cdot \triangle \cdot \triangle = 3125$

17. $\triangle \cdot \triangle = 33.64$

18. $\triangle \cdot \triangle \cdot \triangle = 42.875$

19. $\sqrt{\triangle} = 12$

20. $\sqrt{\triangle} = 27$

In Exercises 21–24, replace each $\boxed{?}$ with $>$, $<$, or $=$.

21. $4^2 \boxed{?} 2^4$

22. $3^5 \boxed{?} 5^3$

23. $7^3 \boxed{?} 3^7$

24. $3^2 \boxed{?} 2^3$

25. The floor plan at the right shows three square rooms. The area of the kitchen is 400 square feet. The area of the bathroom is 64 square feet. The perimeter of the living room is 112 feet. Find the perimeter of both the kitchen and the bathroom, and find the area of the living room. Then find the total floor area.

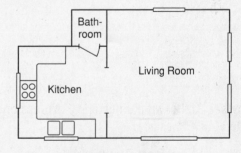

26. The closed box shown at right has dimensions 8 in. by 8 in. by 8 in.

   a. Find the volume of the box.

   b. What is the surface area of the box?

   c. Is it possible to place another box of volume 420 cubic inches inside of the box shown? Explain.

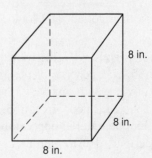

In Exercises 1–14, evaluate the expression without using a calculator.

1. $3 + 8 \div 2$

2. $18 - 6 \div 2$

3. $4 \cdot 3 + 4^2$

4. $6^2 - 9 \cdot 4$

5. $(3 + 2) \div 5 \cdot 2^3$

6. $30 - 3^2 + 4 \cdot 5$

7. $3[2^4 \div 4 - 2]$

8. $16 \div 8(2) \times 6$

9. $24 + 4^2 \cdot 6$

10. $64 \div (2)(8) + 12$

11. $[2 + 3(2) + 3^2] - 4^2$

12. $(4 + 6) \div 2 + 5^2$

13. $24 + (3^2 \div 3) \cdot 11$

14. $[(4^2 + 2) \div 2 + 10] - 2$

In Exercises 15–22, use a calculator to evaluate the expression.

15. $36 + 3 \div 12 + 6$

16. $12 - 3^2 + 9 \cdot 6$

17. $100 \cdot 5 \div 5^3$

18. $20 - (2^5 \div 4^2) \cdot 6$

19. $50 - (2 \div 5^2) \cdot 100$

20. $75 + 5^3 - 4^3 \div 2^3$

21. $24 + (2 \cdot 8)^2 \div 4^2 - 6$

22. $18 \cdot 2^3 - 5 \cdot 6 \div 2$

In Exercises 23–30, decide whether the number sentence is true or false according to the established order of operations. If it is false, insert parentheses to make it true.

23. $4 + 24 \div 6 = 8$

24. $18 - 6 \div 2 = 6$

25. $6 \cdot 3 - 2 \cdot 3 = 18$

26. $24 - 3 \div 7 + 2 = 5$

27. $5 + 2^2 \div 3 = 3$

28. $8^2 - 4 \div 2 + 2 = 64$

29. $24 \div 4 + 2 - 2^2 = 0$

30. $4^2 - 3^2 \div 3 = 13$

In Exercises 31–34, write a numerical expression for the phrase. Then evaluate your expression.

31. 36 divided by the sum of 9 and 3

32. 6 added to the quotient of 42 and 21

33. 42 divided by the quotient of 14 and 2

34. 12 minus the product of 4 and 2

35. You and three friends go to the movies. The group has $40 total. The cost per ticket is $5.25. Each one of the group wants a large soda for $1.25 each, and a box of candy for $1.15 each. Two of the four are willing to share a large buttered popcorn for $3.75 and the other two are going to share a medium unbuttered popcorn for $3.00. Write an expression that represents the total. How much money did the group spend? How much money remains?

Name _____

In Exercises 1–12, evaluate the expression for $x = 2$.

1. $x + 2$

2. $42 \div x$

3. $3x$

4. $x \cdot 4x$

5. $4x^2 - 2$

6. $3x^2 \cdot 2x$

7. $(x - 1) \cdot x^2$

8. $3(2 - x)$

9. $5 \cdot x^2 - 2 \cdot x$

10. $(x + 3)^2$

11. $(7 + x - 1) \div x$

12. $(7 - x)^2$

In Exercises 13–24, evaluate the expression for $a = 2$ and $b = 5$.

13. $b - a$

14. $a^2 \cdot b$

15. $3a + 2b$

16. $(12a - b)$

17. $(a + b)^2$

18. $(2b - a)^2$

19. $(5 + a)^2 + b$

20. $b(9 + a)$

21. $3b + 2a^2$

22. $(4b) \div (2a)$

23. $(2a + b) \div (b - a)$

24. $(a + b^2) \div (b - a)$

In Exercises 25–28, evaluate the expression for $x = 4$, $y = 8$, and $z = 9$.

25. $x + y - z$

26. $y + (z - x)$

27. $x \cdot z \div (y - x)$

28. $y(z - x) + z$

In Exercises 29–32, match the algebraic expression with its verbal description.

a. $x + 5$ **b.** $y \div 5$ **c.** $5a$ **d.** $b - 5$

29. The product of a number and 5

30. The difference of a number and 5

31. The sum of a number and 5

32. The quotient of a number and 5

33. If the expression $3x + 9$ has a value of 15, what is the value of x?

34. If the expression $15y - 4$ has a value of 41, what is the value of y?

35. The cost of admittance to an amusement park is $8.00 per adult and $6.00 per child under the age of 12. Let a represent the number of adults and let c represent the number of children.

   a. Write an expression for the total amount of money a group of both adults and children will cost.

   b. If there are 5 adults and 12 children in one group, how much does it cost the group for admittance?

36. You and two friends are in a canoe on a large lake. If the three of you together can paddle at a speed of 4 mph,

   a. how far could you travel in 75 minutes?

   b. how many minutes would it take to travel 10 miles?

37. The area of a large rectangular field is 12,750 square yards. The width is 150 feet.

   a. Find the length of the field in yards.

   b. What is the length of the field in feet?

   c. What is the area of the field in square feet?

The table gives the top five grossing films of 1992, its distributor, and their box-office gross income in millions. (Source: The Universal Almanac)

Rank	Title	Distributor	Box-office Gross
1	Batman Returns	Warner Brothers	$162.8
2	Lethal Weapon 3	Warner Brothers	$144.7
3	Sister Act	Buena Vista	$139.5
4	Home Alone 2 - Lost in New York	20th Century Fox	$124.9
5	Wayne's World	Paramount	$121.4

1. Which movie earned 139.5 million dollars?

2. How much more money did Batman Returns earn than Wayne's World?

3. What was the total earnings for Warner Brothers by the top two movies of 1992?

The bar graph at the right shows the Men's NCAA champions in wrestling from 1970-1993, and the number of times each school has won.

(Source: The Universal Almanac)

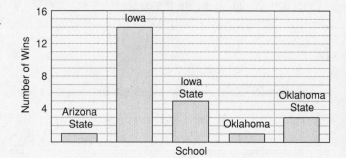

4. Which university has won the most NCAA championships since 1970?

5. Has Iowa won more than the other schools combined since 1970? If so, how many more?

6. Would you say that one university has dominated NCAA wrestling over the past 23 years?

7. Would a table better represent this data? Explain why or why not.

The line graph at the right represents the average monthly snowfall in inches for Minneapolis-St. Paul, Minnesota.

(Source: The Universal Almanac)

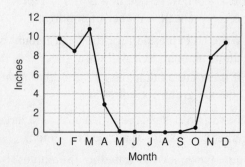

8. Use the graph to determine the month with the most snowfall.

9. Approximately how many inches fall in that month?

10. Estimate the average annual snowfall for Minneapolis-St. Paul.

11. Would you say that the graph shows the fact that it never snows in May, June, July, August, or September? Explain.

In Exercises 1–4, name the polygon.

1.

2.

3.

4.

In Exercises 5–8, decide whether the figure is a polygon. If it is, name it. If it is not, explain why.

5.

6.

7.

8.

9. Draw a quadrilateral with sides of different lengths.

10. Draw a hexagon with four sides equal in measure.

11. Draw an octagon with all sides equal in measure.

In Exercises 12–18, complete the table. All polygons in the table are considered to be regular.

	Type of Polygon	Number of sides	Sum of interior angles	Measure of one interior angle	Number of vertices	Total number of diagonals
12.	Triangle					
13.		8				
14.			1260°			
15.				90°		
16.					6	
17.						5
18.	Decagon					

In Exercises 19–22, decide whether the outer edge of the sign is a polygon. If it is not, explain why it isn't.

19.

20.

21.

22.

In Exercises 1–6, create a table showing your calculations.

1. Calculate the product of 55 and the first 7 whole numbers.

2. Calculate the quotient of 720 and the first 6 natural numbers.

3. Evaluate the fraction of the form $\dfrac{n}{5}$ for the values of n from 1 through 9.

4. Evaluate the fraction of the form $\dfrac{4}{n}$ for the values of n from 1 through 9. What values of n produce repeating decimals?

5. Evaluate $\dfrac{n+1}{n}$ for the first 7 natural numbers.

6. Evaluate $\dfrac{n(n+1)}{2}$ for the first 5 whole numbers.

In Exercises 7 and 8, use a calculator to evaluate the expressions. Then describe the pattern.

7. $5(1) + 1$
   $5(2) + 2$
   $5(3) + 3$
   $5(4) + 4$
   $5(5) + 5$
   $5(6) + 6$
   $5(7) + 7$

8. $1 + 1(101)$
   $2 + 2(101)$
   $3 + 3(101)$
   $4 + 4(101)$
   $5 + 5(101)$
   $6 + 6(101)$
   $7 + 7(101)$

In Exercises 9–12, write the keystrokes that will produce the given sequence on your calculator. Then write the next four numbers in the sequence.

9. 2, 11, 20, 29, ?, ?, ?, ?

10. 4, 12, 36, 108, ?, ?, ?, ?

11. 6, 30, 150, 750, ?, ?, ?, ?

12. 6144, 1536, 384, 96, ?, ?, ?, ?

In Exercises 13–16, use the following.

The sum of the first n odd natural numbers is equal to n^2. For example, for $n = 4$, $1 + 3 + 5 + 7 = 4^2 = 16$. In general, $1 + 3 + 5 + \cdots + (2n - 1) = n^2$ where $2n - 1$ is the nth odd number. Find the following sums.

13. $1 + 3 + 5 + \cdots + 99(n = 50)$

14. $1 + 3 + 5 + \cdots + 999(n = 500)$

15. $1 + 3 + 5 + \cdots + 501(n = 251)$

16. $1 + 3 + 5 + \cdots + 10001(n = 5001)$

2.1

Name _____

In Exercises 1 and 2, write the dimensions of the rectangle and an expression for its area. Then use the Distributive Property to rewrite the expression.

1.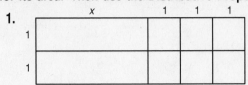

2.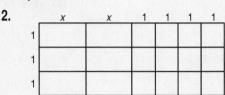

In Exercises 3 and 4, use the Distributive Property to write an equivalent expression. Illustrate your result with an algebraic tile sketch.

3. $3(x + 1)$ **4.** $5(4x + 2)$

In Exercises 5–16, use the Distributive Property to rewrite the expression.

5. $2(3 + 5)$ **6.** $12(4 + 7)$ **7.** $3(x + 2)$

8. $15(y + 4)$ **9.** $4(z + 3)$ **10.** $8(2 + p)$

11. $x(y + 3)$ **12.** $a(c + 4)$ **13.** $2(x + y + z)$

14. $z(a + 4 + b)$ **15.** $f(g + 3 + h)$ **16.** $10(2 + y + z)$

In Exercises 17–19, use a calculator to evaluate the expression two ways.

17. $4(2.5 + 5.2)$ **18.** $12(6.25 + 7.01)$ **19.** $575(10.2 + 25.02)$

20. You have taken two part-time summer jobs. One pays $56 per week and the other $22.50 per week.

    a. Write a verbal model that represents how much you earn over sixteen weeks of summer vacation.

    b. Use the model in Part a to determine how much you earn during summer vacation.

21. You want to buy a new mountain bike, a CD player and a pair of rollerblades. The monthly payments are $26.50, $21.25 and $17.50 respectively.

    a. Write a verbal model that represents the total amount you pay for all three in one year.

    b. Use the model in Part a to determine the amount you pay in one year.

In Exercises 1–9, simplify the expression.

1. $3x + x$

2. $4y + 5y$

3. $2z + 6z + 10$

4. $3a + 5b + 6a$

5. $3z + 7 + 6z + 2$

6. $15z + 5 + 6z$

7. $3s + 2t + 8s + 4$

8. $12x + 3y + 4 + 6y$

9. $6x + 2 + 4x + 9$

In Exercises 10–18, simplify the expression.

10. $4a + 6a + 2a^2$

11. $5z + 2z + 6z^2$

12. $x^3 + 2x^2 + x^3$

13. $3(y + 2) + 6y$

14. $8(z + 1) + 2(z + 4)$

15. $6(st + 2) + 4st$

16. $3(x + z) + 4(z + 2)$

17. $4(x + 2) + 3(y + 6)$

18. $a(b + 2) + 3ab + 4$

In Exercises 19–24, simplify the expression. Then evaluate when $x = 3$ and $y = 4$.

19. $3x + 2y + 6x$

20. $y + 2(y + 2)$

21. $5(x + y) + 2x$

22. $(3 + x)y + x^2$

23. $xy + x^2 + x^2$

24. $3(x + y) + 2(x + y)$

In Exercises 25 and 26, write an expression for the perimeter. Find the perimeter when x is 1, 2, 3, 4 and 5. Represent your results with a table. Then describe the pattern.

25.

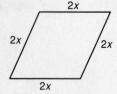

26.

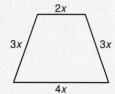

27. You and your family and your best friend and her family are planning a trip to an amusement park. There are two parents and three children in your friend's family, and there is one parent and two children in your family. The price of admission to the park is x dollars for adults and y dollars for youths.

 a. Write an expression for the cost of admission for your family.

 b. Write an expression for the cost of admission for your friend's family.

 c. Write an expression for the total cost for both families combined.

 d. If the price of admission increases from x to $a + 1$ for adults and from y to $b + 2$ for youths, write a new expression for the cost for both families combined. Simplify this expression.

In Exercises 1–4, match the equation with a solution.

a. 2   **b.** 5   **c.** 3   **d.** 1

1. $3x - 4 = 11$ **2.** $y^2 + 4 = 13$ **3.** $8 - 3y = 5$ **4.** $16x^2 = 64$

In Exercises 5 and 6, write the equation as a question. Then solve it mentally.

5. $3x = 36$ **6.** $z - 5 = 3$

In Exercises 7 and 8, write the question as an equation. Then solve it mentally.

7. What number can be added to 5 to obtain 19?   **8.** What number can be divided by 8 to obtain 7?

In Exercises 9–12, decide whether $x = 6$ is a solution of the equation. If it isn't, use mental math to find its solution.

9. $2x = 8$ **10.** $19 - x = 13$ **11.** $\dfrac{30}{x} = 5$ **12.** $3(x + 2) = 18$

In Exercises 13 and 14, decide whether the equations have the same solutions. Explain your reasoning.

13. a. $3x = 12$
      b. $\dfrac{12}{x} = 3$

14. a. $12 - x = 8$
      b. $x - 8 = 12$

In Exercises 15–18, solve the equation using mental math. Check your solution.

15. $m + 6 = 11$ **16.** $n - 6 = 7$ **17.** $18 + p = 42$ **18.** $q - 16 = 35$

In Exercises 19 and 20, decide whether the equation is an identity or a conditional equation. Explain your reasoning.

19. $32 - x = 20$ **20.** $9(x + 3) = 9x + 27$

In Exercises 21–23, use algebra to answer the question. Then use the graph at the right to check your answer. (Source: The Universal Almanac)

21. The number of farms in 1870 was 2.7 million. The number in 1910 was 3.7 million more than the number in 1870. How many farms were there in 1910?

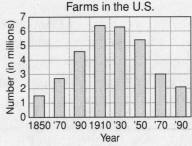

22. The number in 1950 was two times the number in 1870. How many farms were there in 1950?

23. The number in 1930 divided by the number in 1990 is 3. The number in 1990 was 2.1 million. How many farms were there in 1930?

Name _____

In Exercises 1–4, copy and complete the solution.

1.
$$x + 21 = 65$$
$$x + 21 - \boxed{?} = 65 - \boxed{?}$$
$$x = \boxed{?}$$

2.
$$58 = y - 32$$
$$58 + \boxed{?} = y - 32 + \boxed{?}$$
$$\boxed{?} = y$$

3.
$$z - 28 = 101$$
$$z - 28 + \boxed{?} = 101 + \boxed{?}$$
$$z = \boxed{?}$$

4.
$$312 = w + 217$$
$$312 - \boxed{?} = w + 217 - \boxed{?}$$
$$\boxed{?} = w$$

In Exercises 5–13, solve the equation. Then check your solution.

5. $K + 25 = 48$

6. $m + 17 = 71$

7. $n - 23 = 43$

8. $410 = s - 208$

9. $617 + t = 694$

10. $u - 3.7 = 11.2$

11. $7.52 = v + 4.08$

12. $w - 2.5 = 6.2$

13. $x + 2.51 = 7$

In Exercises 14–19, use a calculator to solve the equation.

14. $w - 12.31 = 49.69$

15. $312.27 = x - 210.08$

16. $3.218 = y - 7.011$

17. $z + 2.08 = 13.01$

18. $a + 4.21 = 101.23$

19. $5386.01 = b - 32.07$

In Exercises 20–23, write an equation that represents the statement. Then solve the equation.

20. The difference of x and 7 is 28.

21. The sum of y and 2.7 is 8.3.

22. The sum of z and 3.1 is 15.2.

23. The difference of a and 5.01 is 22.7.

In Exercises 24–26, use the following information.

The 1992 NFL rushing leaders were Emmitt Smith, Barry Foster, Thurman Thomas and Barry Sanders, who rushed for 1352 yards.

(Source: The Universal Almanac)

24. The difference between Emmitt Smith's total and Barry Sanders' total was 361 yards. Find Emmitt Smith's total.

25. The sum of Thurman Thomas' total and Barry Sanders' total was 2839 yards. Find Thurman Thomas' total.

26. 23 yards was the difference of Emmitt Smith's total and Barry Foster's total. Find Barry Foster's total.

2.5

Name _____

In Exercises 1 and 2, write the equation as a verbal sentence. Then solve the equation.

1. $5x = 10$

2. $\dfrac{z}{2} = 11$

In Exercises 3–18, solve the equation. Check your solution.

3. $3x = 15$

4. $11y = 110$

5. $81 = 9z$

6. $35 = 7a$

7. $8 = \dfrac{b}{9}$

8. $\dfrac{c}{4} = 5$

9. $\dfrac{d}{7} = 3$

10. $\dfrac{m}{5} = 12$

11. $6p = 132$

12. $9q = 23.4$

13. $7.5x = 337.5$

14. $16t = 540$

15. $\dfrac{v}{5.2} = 3$

16. $5.5w = 247.5$

17. $\dfrac{x}{3.2} = 16$

18. $\dfrac{y}{15} = 3.2$

In Exercises 19–26, use a calculator to solve the equation.

19. $523x = 2092$

20. $489z = 1467$

21. $34w = 306$

22. $65t = 390$

23. $\dfrac{x}{6} = 958$

24. $\dfrac{y}{8} = 605$

25. $\dfrac{z}{19} = 203$

26. $\dfrac{w}{621} = 31$

In Exercises 27–30, solve for x.

27.

x	Area is 28 square units

7

28.

x	Area is 54 square units

9

29.

4 | Area is 68 square units |

x

30.

7 | Area is 98 square units |

x

In Exercises 31 and 32, write an equation that represents the sentence. Then solve the equation.

31. The number of motorcycles m times 5 equals 45 cycles.

32. The product of the number of compact discs c and 8 is 56 discs.

33. Walter Payton is the All-Time Pro Football rushing leader. He averaged approximately 4.368 yards per carry. Walter attempted 3838 carries over his 13 year career. (Source: Universal Almanac)

   a. Write a verbal model that represents his total yards.

   b. Write an algebraic model that represents his total yards. Then solve the equation.

In Exercises 1–4, match the verbal phrase with its algebraic expression.

a. $2m + 4$ **b.** $\dfrac{n}{2} - 4$ **c.** $10 - p$ **d.** $y - 10$

1. 4 more than twice a number

2. The difference of 10 and a number

3. 4 less than the quotient of a number and 2

4. 10 less than a number

In Exercises 5–15, translate the verbal phrase into an algebraic expression.

5. 16 plus a number

6. A number divided by 12

7. The quotient of a number and 11

8. 8 times a number

9. 12 less than a number

10. 14 more than 6 times a number

11. 8 minus the product of 5 and a number

12. The sum of 3 times a number and 17

13. The product of 6 and 4 more than a number

14. The quotient of a number and 4 more than another number

15. The difference of 3 times a number an 6 times another number

In Exercises 16–19, write an algebraic expression.

16. Your allowance plus $5.00

17. 5 years older than your sister

18. Number of players divided by 4

19. 5 times more than the cost to her

In Exercises 20–23, write an algebraic expression that represents the phrase. Let a represent your age now.

20. Your age 6 years ago

21. One-third your age

22. 4 times your age

23. Your age 14 years from now

24. Suppose you purchased a new mountain bike by making a down payment of $38.70 plus monthly payments of $5.75 each.

   a. Write an algebraic expression that represents your total cost. Let m be the number of monthly payments.

   b. Find the cost if you have to make 30 monthly payments.

In Exercises 1–4, match the sentence with an equation.

a. $x - 6 = 12$ **b.** $\dfrac{x}{6} = 12$ **c.** $6x = 12$ **d.** $12 - x = 6$

1. The difference of 12 and x is 6.

2. The quotient of x and 6 is 12.

3. 12 equals the difference of x and 6.

4. The product of 6 and x is 12.

In Exercises 5–8, write an algebraic equation that represents the verbal sentence. Then solve the equation.

5. The number of cassettes decreased by 5 is 13.

6. $225.75 is the cost of 3 calculators at x dollars each.

7. The number of books divided by 7 equals 9.

8. 32 is the sum of 18 sweatshirts and y.

In Exercises 9–12, write a verbal sentence that represents the equation.

9. $a - 6 = 13$

10. $45 = 5c$

11. $\dfrac{e}{5} = 40$

12. $15 = 3 + f$

In Exercises 13–15, use a verbal model, labels, and an algebraic model to answer the question.

13. The quotient of a number and 6 is 21. Find the number.

14. 165 is the product of a number and 11. Find the number.

15. On a recent trip to an audio-video store you purchased four items. The total cost was $39.00. Three items you purchased were for yourself, and the last your sister asked you to buy for her. She now wants to pay you back but you lost the receipt. However, you do know that the three items you purchased for yourself were a cassette single for $2.50, a cassette for $6.50 and a CD for $13.50. How much does your sister owe you for her item?

In Exercises 1–6, consider the following question.

You are fencing a rectangular corral to keep horses. The region's length is 48 more feet than its width. The perimeter of the region is 184 feet. What are the dimensions of the region?

1. Write a verbal model that relates the length, the width and the perimeter.

2. Assign labels to the three parts of your model.

3. Use the labels to translate your verbal model into an algebraic model.

4. Solve the algebraic model.

5. Answer the question.

6. If the cost of fencing is $5 per foot, what is the cost of fencing the region?

In Exercises 7–11, consider the following question.

You are a salesperson at the local sporting goods store. Your monthly earnings are a combination of your monthly base salary plus your sales commission. Your monthly salary is $300 and your sales commission is $\frac{1}{25}$ of your monthly sales. How much did you make during a month when your sales totaled $2600.

7. Write a verbal model that relates your sales commission rate, your sales commission and your monthly sales.

8. Assign labels to each part of your model.

9. Use the labels to translate your verbal model into an algebraic model.

10. Solve the algebraic model.

11. Answer the original question.

In Exercises 12 and 13, decide which information is necessary to solve the problem. Then solve the problem.

12. Everyday but Saturday and Sunday, your mother travels 16 miles one way to work. She works from 7 A.M. to 4 P.M. How many miles does she travel back and forth to work each week?

13. Each morning your brother gets up at 6:30 A.M. and runs about 3 miles in approximately 30 minutes. He does this no matter what the weather 7 days a week, 52 weeks a year. Approximately how many miles does he run per week?

In Exercises 1–6, state two solutions of the inequality.

1. $x \geq 3$

2. $y < 1.5$

3. $36 < x$

4. $300 \geq z$

5. $a < 11.5$

6. $b \geq 0.01$

In Exercises 7–18, solve the inequality. Check the answer.

7. $x + 3 < 8$

8. $y - 2 \geq 10$

9. $3z < 15$

10. $\dfrac{a}{2} > 11$

11. $b - 4 < 6$

12. $15 > c - 12$

13. $4p < 60$

14. $\dfrac{q}{4} > 12.2$

15. $x - 2.5 < 7.2$

16. $42 > \dfrac{c}{7}$

17. $105.5 \geq y - 5$

18. $11.2 < 4z$

In Exercises 19–22, write an inequality that represents the sentence. Then solve the inequality.

19. d minus 5 is less than or equal to 4.25.

20. The sum of y and 7 is greater than 10.

21. x times 40 is less than 120.

22. 69 is greater than the product of a and 3.

In Exercises 23–26, write a sentence that represents the inequality.

23. $e - 4 > 6$

24. $5 + f \leq 10$

25. $28 < 7r$

26. $17r < 102$

In Exercises 27–30, state whether the inequality $x > 2.1$ is true for the value of x.

27. 2.01

28. 20

29. 0.21

30. 2.1

In Exercises 31–34, consider the following question.

Suppose you are taking a senior level calculus course in which the grade is based on 6 100-point exams. To earn an A in this course, you must have at least 540 points total. On the first five exams your scores were 85, 92, 88, 96, and 87. How many points do you have to obtain on the sixth test in order to earn an A in the course?

31. Write a verbal model that relates your scores so far, the score on the sixth test and the point total necessary to earn an A.

32. Translate your verbal model into an algebraic model.

33. Solve the algebraic model.

34. Suppose you scored a 93 on your sixth test. Did you earn an A? Explain.

3.1

Name _____

In Exercises 1 and 2, draw a number line and plot the integers.

1. $-3, 1, -2$ **2.** $0, 5, -1$

In Exercises 3–8, compare the integers using the symbols < or >.

3. 2 ☐ 4   **4.** -3 ☐ 3   **5.** 0 ☐ -4

6. 5 ☐ -2 **7.** -1 ☐ -3 **8.** -18 ☐ -14

In Exercises 9–14, write the opposite and absolute value of the integer.

9. 3   **10.** -2 **11.** 5

12. -6 **13.** -10 **14.** -100

In Exercises 15–18, write the integer that represents the situation.

15. 700 feet above sea level   **16.** A loss of 57 dollars

17. A 15 yard gain   **18.** A gain of 20 pounds

In Exercises 19–22, order the integers from least to greatest.

19. $-6, 5, -4, 3, 2$ **20.** $-10, 8, -7, 6, 0$

21. $-2, 2, -3, 4, 1$ **22.** $-1, 1, 0, 2, -3$

In Exercises 23–26, use the number line to estimate the number of days between the events.

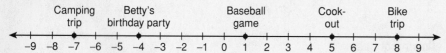

23. Bike trip and cook out   **24.** Birthday party and cook out

25. Baseball game and bike trip   **26.** Birthday party and camping trip

In Exercises 27–29, use the following:

On a certain day in January the temperatures in Anchorage, Alaska was 15° below zero. In St. Paul, Minnesota it was 5° above zero. In San Diego, California, it was 50° above zero. And in Tampa, Florida, it was 75° above zero.

27. Draw a vertical number line showing these temperatures.

28. How much warmer is it in Tampa than in St. Paul?

29. How much colder is it in Anchorage than in San Diego?

In Exercises 1–12, find the sum. Write your conclusion as an equation.

1. $3 + 12$

2. $-6 + (-3)$

3. $-12 + (-12)$

4. $6 + 16$

5. $-5 + 5$

6. $12 + (-18)$

7. $-19 + 12$

8. $26 + (-26)$

9. $4 + 0$

10. $0 + (-11)$

11. $15 + (-2)$

12. $-12 + 0$

In Exercises 13–15, complete the statement. Then describe the pattern.

13. $5 + (-3) = \square$

$5 + (-2) = \square$

$5 + (-1) = \square$

$5 + \quad 0 = \square$

$5 + \quad 1 = \square$

14. $-3 + \quad 3 = \square$

$-3 + \quad 2 = \square$

$-3 + \quad 1 = \square$

$-3 + \quad 0 = \square$

$-3 + (-1) = \square$

15. $2 + (-6) = \square$

$2 + (-4) = \square$

$2 + (-2) = \square$

$2 + \quad 0 = \square$

$2 + \quad 2 = \square$

In Exercises 16–18, find three sets of values of x and y that make the equation true. (There are many correct answers.)

16. $x + y = 6$

17. $x + y = -4$

18. $x + y = -10$

In Exercises 19–21, use mental math to solve the equation.

19. $3 + x = -6$

20. $-4 + z = -2$

21. $-3 + m = 10$

In Exercises 22 and 23, match the equation with the real life situation. Then solve the equation for x and explain what x represents in the problem.

a. You have 100 dollars in a savings account and you withdraw 30 dollars.

b. A submarine is 100 feet below sea level. It ascends 30 feet.

22. $-100 + 30 = x$

23. $100 - 30 = x$

In Exercises 24 and 25, write a real life situation that can be represented by the equation.

24. $10 + (-5) = x$

25. $-25 + 10 = x$

In Exercises 26 and 27, find a pair of integers whose sum is -2. (Use the integers labeled $a, b, c,$ and d.)

26.

27.

In Exercises 1–9, find the sum. Write your conclusion as an equation.

1. $6 + (-2) + (-8)$

2. $-6 + (-2) + 10$

3. $6 + (-7) + (-8)$

4. $-16 + 15 + (-3)$

5. $-10 + 11 + (-2)$

6. $-10 + 6 + (-8)$

7. $-10 + (-6) + (-15)$

8. $6 + (-5) + (-4)$

9. $10 + (-2) + 13$

In Exercises 10–13, use a calculator to find the sum.

10. $-51 + 110 + (-37) + (-87)$

11. $112 + (-34) + (-38) + 115$

12. $104 + (-231) + (-325) + 110$

13. $251 + (-321) + (-45) + 68$

In Exercises 14 and 15, decide whether the sum is positive or negative. Explain how you can make your decision without actually finding the sum.

14. $215 + (-312) + 43$

15. $-38 + 115 + (-42)$

In Exercises 16–25, simplify the expression. Then evaluate the expression when $x = 3$.

16. $-6x + 10x + (-2x)$

17. $17x + (-6x) + 4$

18. $20x + (-16x) + (-2x)$

19. $-3x + 12x + 10$

20. $6x + (-2x) + x + 7$

21. $6 + (-3x) + 11x$

22. $4x + (-x) + (-2x)$

23. $9x + 6 + (-3x) + 2$

24. $15x + (-3x) + 7x + 4$

25. $11x + (-6x) + 11$

In Exercises 26–31, complete the statement using >, <, or =.

26. $-8 \ \boxed{} \ -10 + (-2)$

27. $7 + (-3) \ \boxed{} \ -8 + (-2)$

28. $-6 + (-2) \ \boxed{} \ -4$

29. $-5 + (-6) \ \boxed{} \ -6 + 5$

30. $-11 \ \boxed{} \ -8 + 19$

31. $10 + (-2) \ \boxed{} \ -9 + 1$

32. On Monday you purchased $100 worth of stock. The value of the stock on Monday was $6 per share. Tuesday it rose $2. Wednesday it fell $4. Thursday it rose $3. Friday is fell $2. What is the week ending price per share?

33. You are in an elevator in a 50 story building. You are on the 25th floor. You remain on the elevator as passengers get on and off. What floor are you on an hour later, if the elevator moves as follows: up 12, down 23, up 35, down 12, down 3, and up 16?

In Exercises 1–9, find the difference. Write your conclusion as an equation.

1. $3 - 7$

2. $-4 - (-3)$

3. $6 - (-8)$

4. $10 - (-2)$

5. $-23 - 2$

6. $12 - (-8)$

7. $14 - (-3)$

8. $16 - (-16)$

9. $-16 - 16$

In Exercises 10–15, evaluate the expression when $a = 2$ and when $a = -2$.

10. $a - 3$

11. $3 - a$

12. $a - 2$

13. $6 - a$

14. $a - a$

15. $a + a$

In Exercises 16 and 17, rewrite the expression as a sum. Then identify the terms of the expression.

16. $4x - 2x + 8$

17. $10x - 12 - 5$

In Exercises 18–23, simplify the expression.

18. $2x - 8x - 7$

19. $11m - 2m + 2$

20. $-12y - (-3y) - 3$

21. $-30x - 25x - 3x$

22. $-4z - (-16z)$

23. $6 - (-2m) - 3m$

In Exercises 24–27, use a calculator to evaluate the expression.

24. $-20 - 37 - (-81)$

25. $116 - 231 - (-324)$

26. $6 - 6 - (-6)$

27. $-6 - (-6) - 6$

In Exercises 28 and 29, find values for a and b so that the statement is true. (There are many correct answers.)

28. a is positive, b is positive, and $b - a$ is negative.

29. a is negative, b is negative, and $b - a$ is positive.

In Exercises 30–32, use the table which shows the highest and lowest elevations on the continents. Positive numbers are elevations in feet above sea level and negative numbers are elevations in feet below sea level.

Continent	Highest point	Feet above sea level	Lowest point	Feet below sea level
Asia	Mt. Everest	29,028	Dead Sea	−1312
North America	Mt. McKinley	20,320	Death Valley	−282
Africa	Mt. Kilimanjaro	19,340	Lake Assal	−512
Europe	Mt. Elbrus	18,510	Caspian Sea	−92

30. Find the difference between the highest point and lowest point on each continent.

31. Find the difference between the lowest points in Asia and North America.

32. Find the difference between the highest points in Africa and Europe.

Extra Practice 3.5

Name _____

In Exercises 1–9, find the product. Write your conclusion as an equation.

1. $6 \cdot 5$

2. $8(10)$

3. $-3 \cdot (-2)$

4. $-15 \cdot 3$

5. $10 \cdot (-3)$

6. $7 \cdot (-4)$

7. $(-3)(-7)$

8. $(0)(-30)$

9. $(4)(0)$

In Exercises 10–12, simplify the expression.

10. $-8 \cdot (-y)$

11. $10 \cdot (-a)$

12. $(-11)(-w)$

In Exercises 13–15, evaluate the expression when $x = 3$ and $y = -4$.

13. xy

14. $x^2 y$

15. $-y$

In Exercises 16–21, find the product.

16. $(-1)(-3)(-4)$

17. $(-3)(-4)(5)$

18. $(3)(-5)(2)$

19. $(-4)(-2)(3)$

20. $(5)(-2)(-3)$

21. $(-6)(2)(-3)$

In Exercises 22–27, use a calculator to find the product.

22. $(-13)(-27)$

23. $(42)(-101)$

24. $(-39)(-102)$

25. $\frac{5}{8}(-64)$

26. $\frac{9}{11}(-121)$

27. $(43)(-6)(-7)$

In Exercises 28–33, use mental math to solve the equation.

28. $3x = -27$

29. $-5n = 25$

30. $6y = -60$

31. $-11k = -33$

32. $2m = -24$

33. $-7p = -35$

In Exercises 34–36, use the rectangle at the right. The rectangle has an area of 24 square units. The base of the rectangle rests on a number line.

34. If $b = -2$, what is a?

35. If $b = 2$, what is a?

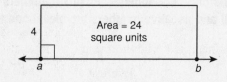

36. If $b = -10$, what is a?

37. You are watching a Canadian television station and the weather report begins. The weatherman reports that the high and low temperatures for the day were $5°C$ and $-10°C$. Convert these temperatures to Fahrenheit. Use the model from the text.

3.6

Name _____

In Exercises 1–9, evaluate the expression. Check your results by multiplying.

1. $\dfrac{96}{3}$

2. $\dfrac{180}{4}$

3. $\dfrac{-512}{16}$

4. $-208 \div (-8)$

5. $288 \div (-16)$

6. $\dfrac{0}{-36}$

7. $0 \div 327$

8. $-1008 \div (-21)$

9. $2730 \div (-65)$

In Exercises 10 and 11, complete the statement. Then describe the pattern.

10. $-36 \div 2 = \square$

    $-34 \div 2 = \square$

    $-32 \div 2 = \square$

    $-30 \div 2 = \square$

    $-28 \div 2 = \square$

11. $-2 \div (-1) = \square$

    $-3 \div (-1) = \square$

    $-4 \div (-1) = \square$

    $-5 \div (-1) = \square$

    $-6 \div (-1) = \square$

In Exercises 12–14, evaluate when $x = -3$, $y = 2$ and $z = -4$.

12. xz

13. $\dfrac{-6y}{x}$

14. $\dfrac{xz}{y}$

In Exercises 15–20, use mental math to solve the equation.

15. $\dfrac{a}{8} = -2$

16. $\dfrac{c}{-5} = -4$

17. $\dfrac{z}{3} = -6$

18. $\dfrac{w}{-2} = 11$

19. $\dfrac{m}{-6} = 5$

20. $\dfrac{n}{3} = -10$

In Exercises 21 and 22, find the average of the numbers.

21. 18, 11, 15, 17, 13, 16

22. $-8, -6, -5, -8, -7, -2$

In Exercises 23 and 24, use the table which shows the gold medal winners and their times in the women's 100-meter freestyle during the Olympic Games from 1972 through 1992.

Year	Winner	Country	Time in Seconds
1972	Sandra Neilson	United States	58.59
1976	Kornelia Ender	East Germany	55.65
1980	Barbara Krause	East Germany	54.79
1984	Nancy Hogshead	United States	55.92
1988	Kristin Otto	East Germany	54.93
1992	Zhuang Yong	China	54.65

23. Find the average winning time for the last six Summer Olympics.

24. Predict whether the average winning time for the next six Olympic Games will be more or less than your result in Exercise 23. Explain your predictions.

Name _____

In Exercises 1–4, decide whether the value of the variable is a solution of the equation. If not, find the solution.

1. $x + 5 = 8$, $x = 3$

2. $y - 6 = -10$, $y = 4$

3. $-32 = -16b$, $b = 2$

4. $\dfrac{m}{-2} = 24$, $m = -12$

In Exercises 5–16, solve the equation. Check your solution.

5. $c - 5 = -2$

6. $y + 6 = 3$

7. $z - 5 = 12$

8. $-21 = a - 12$

9. $b + 4 = -6$

10. $c - 2 = -10$

11. $-72 = 24d$

12. $-3e = -48$

13. $\dfrac{f}{-3} = -11$

14. $-22 = -11g$

15. $3h = -9$

16. $\dfrac{j}{2} = -8$

In Exercises 17 and 18, write an algebraic equation for the sentence. Then solve the equation and write your conclusion as a sentence.

17. The sum of x and 3 is -6.

18. The product of z and -3 is -27.

In Exercises 19–24, use a calculator to solve the equation. Then check your solution.

19. $-2351 = t + 205$

20. $m - 216 = 3864$

21. $-4428 = -123n$

22. $\dfrac{p}{-23} = 58$

23. $\dfrac{q}{22} = -24$

24. $-32r = -8096$

In Exercises 25–30, match the equation with its solution.

a. -32 **b.** 90 **c.** 0 **d.** -7 **e.** -3 **f.** -6

25. $t - 5 + 2 = -3$

26. $x - 3x = 64$

27. $\dfrac{p}{3} = 41 - 11$

28. $y + 4y = -30 - 5$

29. $\dfrac{-24}{q} = 16 - 12$

30. $2x + 3x = -15$

In Exercises 31 and 32 use the following information.

The bill (including parts and labor) for the repair of an automobile was $357. The cost for parts was $285. Therefore, the total cost of labor was $72. The labor rate was $32 per hour.

31. Use the verbal model

Total cost of labor	=	Cost of labor per hour	·	The number of hours

to write an algebraic model for the cost of labor. Let t represent the number of hours of labor.

32. Determine the number of hours of labor required.

In Exercises 1–6, match the ordered pair with its corresponding point in the coordinate plane. Identify the quadrant in which the point lies.

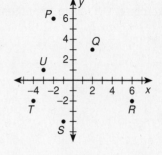

1. $(-1, -4)$

2. $(2, 3)$

3. $(6, -2)$

4. $(-2, 6)$

5. $(-3, 1)$

6. $(-4, -2)$

In Exercises 7–10, plot the points on a single coordinate plane. Determine the quadrant in which the point lies.

7. $(6, -2)$

8. $(3, 4)$

9. $(-2, -5)$

10. $(-3, 2)$

In Exercises 11–14, determine the quadrant in which (x, y) lies.

11. $x < 0$ and $y = -x$

12. $x > 0$ and $y = x$

13. $x < 0$ and $y = x$

14. $x > 0$ and $y = -x$

In Exercises 15 and 16, plot the points on a coordinate plane to form the vertices of a rectangle. Find the area and perimeter of the rectangle.

15. $A(2, 1), B(5, 1), C(2, 2)$, and $D(5, 2)$

16. $A(-1, 5), B(-1, -4), C(3, 5)$, and $D(3, -4)$

In Exercises 17–19, show that the ordered pair is a solution of the equation. Then find three other solutions.

17. $2 + x = y; \ (-12, -10)$

18. $y - 3 = x; \ (6, 9)$

19. $x - y = 10; \ (12, 2)$

In Exercises 20–23, use the following.

The graph shows the value of an automobile, which was purchased new for $25,000, based on the number of years you own it.

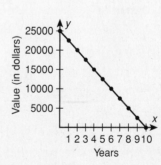

20. After 3 years, what is the value of the car?

21. After 6 years, what is the value of the car?

22. The value is given by the verbal model.

Value	=	Original value	−	$2500	·	Number of years owned

Create an algebraic model from the verbal model. Let t represent the number of years you own the car, and V represent the value of the car.

23. Find three solutions of your equation.

4.1

Name _____

In Exercises 1–9, solve the equation. Then check your solution.

1. $2x - 8 = 10$

2. $3x - 7 = 2$

3. $4x + 1 = -3$

4. $\dfrac{t}{2} - 7 = -3$

5. $\dfrac{z}{3} + 4 = -1$

6. $\dfrac{w}{5} - 2 = -7$

7. $6m - 210 = 6$

8. $2x + \dfrac{1}{3} = \dfrac{13}{3}$

9. $\dfrac{z}{-3} + \dfrac{1}{4} = \dfrac{-3}{4}$

10. Sketch an algebra-tile solution for the equation $2x + 3 = 7$.

In Exercises 11–14, write the sentence as an equation. Then solve it.

11. 2 times a number, plus 3 is 13.

12. 6 times a number, plus 11 is 65.

13. The quotient of a number and 3, plus 2 is -7.

14. A number divided by four, minus 6 is 1.

In Exercises 15 and 16, the upper line segment has the same length as the lower double line segment. Write the implied equation and solve for x.

15.

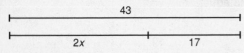

16.

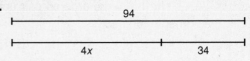

17. The length of a rectangular tennis court is six feet more than twice the width. What is the width of the court if the length is 78 feet?

a. Write a verbal model of the problem.

b. Assign labels to each part of your verbal model.

c. Write and solve the algebraic model of the problem.

d. Answer the question. Then check your equation.

18. Describe a real-life situation that can be modeled by the equation $2x + 5 = 10$.

4.2

Name _____

In Exercises 1–4, decide whether the given value is a solution of the equation. If not, find the solution.

1. $6x - 2x - 3 = 5; x = \frac{1}{2}$

2. $3y + 2 + 5y = -14; y = 2$

3. $5a - 16 + 2a - 2 = -4; a = 2$

4. $-6 = 4 - 2t + 4t + 16; t = -13$

In Exercises 5–13, solve the equation. Check your solution.

5. $6x - 2x + 11 = -5$

6. $3y - 6 - 2y = 6$

7. $36 = 7a - 12 - 10a$

8. $11m - 6 - 5m = 60$

9. $12n - 14n + 6 = 32$

10. $p - 17p - 6 = -38$

11. $3x - 5x + 11x = -81$

12. $11q - 2q - 12q = -39$

13. $\frac{4}{3}x - \frac{10}{3}x - 11 = 1$

In Exercises 14 and 15, write an equation that represents the sentence. Then solve.

14. The sum of $2x$ and $5x$ and $-3x$ and -3 is 9.

15. 11 subtracted from the sum of $7y$ and $2y$ is -38.

In Exercises 16 and 17, use the given information to write an equation. Then solve the equation, and find the angles.

16. The sum of the measures of two supplementary angles is $180°$.

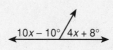

17. The sum of the measures of the angles of a quadrilateral is $360°$.

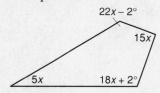

18. You have a summer job as a lifeguard at a pool. The table shows the number of hours you worked each day during a week. During that week, you earned \$323.30. You earn x dollars per hour.

S	M	T	W	T	F	S
8	7	7	4	7	10	10

a. Write an equation that represents the amount you earn per hour.

b. Solve the equation to find the amount you get paid per hour.

In Exercises 1 and 2, describe two different ways to solve the equation.

1. $4x = -24$ **2.** $-3x = -33$

In Exercises 3–14, solve the equation.

3. $3y - 12 = 18$ **4.** $2x + 11 = -19$ **5.** $-\frac{1}{2}z + 7 = -3$

6. $\frac{1}{3}m - 4 = 2$ **7.** $-4t + 6 = -10$ **8.** $18y - 6 = -30$

9. $-13t + 10 = -16$ **10.** $\frac{1}{10}x - 1 = 0$ **11.** $\frac{2}{3}x + \frac{1}{3}x - 6 = 1$

12. $\frac{4}{5}x - \frac{3}{5}x = 2$ **13.** $2(x + 5) = -8$ **14.** $-3(x + 2) = 18$

15. The sum of four times a number and 16 is 100. Find the number. Write an equation and solve it.

16. The difference of three times a number and 23 is 34. Find the number. Write an equation and solve it.

17. The sum of one-half a number and 27 is 40. Find the number. Write an equation and solve it.

18. 13 is the difference of one-fifth a number and 8. Find the number. Write an equation and solve it.

19. A traffic sign has the shape of an equilateral triangle. The perimeter of the sign is 225 centimeters. Find the length of the sides of the sign. (An equilateral triangle is one whose sides have the same length.)

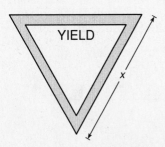

20. A rectangle has a perimeter of 78 inches. Its length is 6 inches more than twice its width.

    a. Make a sketch of the rectangle and label its sides.

    b. Find the rectangles dimensions.

21. In 1992, the salary of the governor of New York was about $25,000 more than three times the salary of the governor of Arkansas. The total of the two salaries was $165,000. Find the 1992 salaries of each state's governor. (Source: The Universal Almanac)

In Exercises 1 and 2, describe the error. Then solve the equation.

1.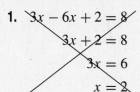

$$3x - 6x + 2 = 8$$
$$3x + 2 = 8$$
$$3x = 6$$
$$x = 2$$

2.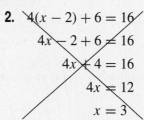

$$4(x - 2) + 6 = 16$$
$$4x - 2 + 6 = 16$$
$$4x + 4 = 16$$
$$4x = 12$$
$$x = 3$$

In Exercises 3–11, solve the equation. Check your solution.

3. $3x + 2(x - 1) = 8$

4. $6 = 3y + 3(y - 6)$

5. $6(2 - r) = -18$

6. $8(p + 1) + 3p = -14$

7. $3(t - 4) + 6 = 0$

8. $6(x - 4) + 3x = 3$

9. $\frac{5}{6}x - \frac{4}{6}x + 2 = -3$

10. $16 = -\frac{1}{2}(q + 2)$

11. $-5(y + 3) = 25$

12. Solve the equation $2(x + 7) = -26$ in two ways.

 a. Use the Distributive Property first.

 b. Multiply by a reciprocal first.

 c. Which way do you prefer? Why?

13. Solve the equation $-\frac{1}{7}(x - 11) = 2$ in two ways.

 a. Use the Distributive Property first.

 b. Multiply by a reciprocal first.

 c. Which way do you prefer? Why?

14. Write an equation for the area of the rectangle. Then solve for x.

x + 5

| 6 | Area is 42 square units |

15. Write an equation, solve the equation for x, and find the measures of the angles.

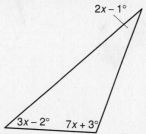

$2x - 1°$

$3x - 2°$ $7x + 3°$

16. A grocer wants to mix x pounds of cashew nuts worth \$7.00 per pound with 9 pounds of peanuts worth \$3.00 per pound to obtain $9 + x$ pounds of mixture worth \$5.00 per pound. Use the verbal model and labels to write an equation and find the number of pounds of cashews required to obtain the specified mixture.

Verbal model

| Total cost of cashews | + | Total cost of peanuts | = | Total cost of mixed nuts |

Labels   Cost per pound of cashews = \$7.00
Number of pounds of cashews = x
Cost per pound of peanuts = \$3.00
Number of pounds of peanuts = 9
Cost per pound of mixed nuts = \$5.00
Number of pounds of mixed nuts = $9 + x$ pounds

In Exercises 1–3, match the equation with its solution.

a. $x = 4$ **b.** $x = 5$ **c.** $x = -8$

1. $3x + 6 = x - 10$

2. $8x + 2 = 6x + 10$

3. $4(x - 1) = x + 11$

In Exercises 4–12, solve the equation. Then check your solution.

4. $5x + 12 = 3x$

5. $-5x + 11 = 6x$

6. $8x + 12 = 4x - 4$

7. $-3x + 2 = -7x - 22$

8. $5(x + 3) = 4(x - 4)$

9. $2(x - 7) = 5(x + 2)$

10. $-11 - 8t = 7(t + 2)$

11. $8(3 - y) = 3y + 2$

12. $10(3x + 1) = 2(10x - 5)$

In Exercises 13 and 14, write the equation implied by the model. Then solve it.

13.

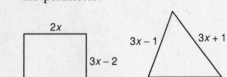

14.

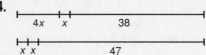

In Exercises 15 and 16, write the equation and find the unknown number.

15. Two less than four times a number is equal to two more than three times the same number.

16. Four times the sum of a number and three is equal to eight more than twice the same number.

17. Find the value of x so that the rectangle and the triangle have the same perimeter. What is the perimeter?

18. Find the value of x so that the figure is a square. What is the length of the sides?

2(x + 4)

4(x − 1)

19. One bacterial culture is 18 days older than a second bacterial culture. In 10 days the first culture will be twice the age of the second. Use the verbal model and the labels to write and solve an algebraic equation. Find the present age of the two cultures.

Verbal model
| Age of first culture in 10 days | $= 2 \cdot$ | Age of second culture in 10 days |

Labels
x = age of second culture
$x + 10$ = age of second culture in 10 days
$x + 18$ = age of first culture
$x + 18 + 10$ = age of first culture in 10 days

4.6

Name _____

In Exercises 1–7, use the following.

One long distance phone company charges $2 for the first minute and $0.15 for each additional minute. Another company charges $2.50 for the first minute and $0.10 for each additional minute. For what length of a phone call would the two companies have the same charge?

1. Show how to use a table and graph to solve the problem.

2. Write a verbal model.

3. Assign labels to each part of the model (Hint: let t represent the length of the phone call, and use $t - 1$ to count the number of minutes after first.)

4. Write an algebraic model.

5. Solve the algebraic model.

6. How long of a phone call will each company have the same charge?

7. How much is that phone call?

8. You own a small business that produces bicycles helmets. You want to determine how many helmets must be sold to break even. Your costs are $2500 plus $12 in materials for each helmet. You sell each helmet for $52. Write an algebraic model. Then solve. How many helmets must you sell to break even?

In Exercises 1 and 2, describe the error. Write a correct solution.

1. $2.5(2.2x + 4.5) = 22.5$

   $5.5x + 11.3 = 22.5$

   $5.5x = 11.2$

   $x \approx 2.04$

2. $0.35(2.45x - 5.82) = 12.64$

   $0.86x - 2.04 = 12.64$

   $0.86x = 14.68$

   $x \approx 17.07$

In Exercises 3–16, use a calculator to solve the equation. Round your answer to two decimal places.

3. $4x + 5 = -9$

4. $12y + 1 = 14$

5. $26x - 4 = 25$

6. $13 - 12t = -7$

7. $3(2x - 4) = -6x + 7$

8. $22x - 4 = 5(7 - 2x)$

9. $1.2x + 21.3 = -4.6$

10. $3.21(4.2x - 5.1) = 18.92$

11. $0.25t - 11.6 = 2.45t$

12. $2.4x + 11.8 = 7.2x - 26.4$

13. $4.2(4.5x - 31.2) = -4.2x$

14. $13.6x - 4.2 = 6.1(2.5x - 4)$

15. $3.25x - 6.7 = -4.2(3.6x - 4.5)$

16. $19.2(3.5 - 4.1x) = 7.2(8.7x - 4.9)$

17. You eat at a fine Italian restaurant. The gratuity (tip) rate is 0.15 and the total bill is $29.50. Let p represent the price of the meal. Solve $p + 0.15p = 29.50$ to find the price of the meal.

18. You purchase an item. The sales tax rate is 0.055 and the total cost is $5.96. Let p represent the price of the item (not including sales tax). Solve $p + 0.055p = 5.96$ to find the price of the item.

19. You wish to eat at a neighborhood diner where the special is 12¢ wings. You have $5. You know you are going to have two sodas for 75¢ each. If you are really hungry, how many wings can you order?

20. You are a salesperson who receives $15 per day for meals and 22¢ per mile driven on the job. Your average reimbursement per day is $27.49. Using this amount, estimate the average number of miles you drive per day.

In Exercises 1–3, solve for x and find the dimensions of the polygon.

1. Square
   Perimeter: 24 units
   Side: $x - 2$

2. Rectangle
   Perimeter: 64 units
   Width: $5x + 2$
   Length: $3x - 2$

3. Regular Pentagon
   Perimeter: 65 units
   Side: $4x + 1$

In Exercises 4 and 5, find the measures of each angle.

4. The sum of the measures of $\angle 1$ and $\angle 2$ is $180°$.

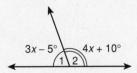

5. The sum of the measures of $\angle 1$, $\angle 2$, and $\angle 3$ is $180°$.

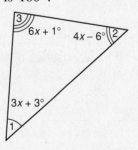

6. Find the area of the swimming pool if the total swimming area, including the sidewalk, is 2400 square feet and the sidewalk is 3 feet wide.

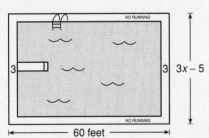

7. Find the area of the triangle if the area of the rectangle is 120 square inches.

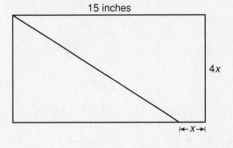

8. Find the area of a rectangular tennis court if the perimeter is 480 feet. The length of the court is six feet more than twice the width.

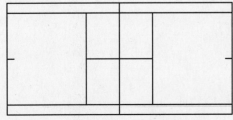

Perimeter = 480 feet

9. Use the map below to approximate the area of Tennessee. Explain your method.

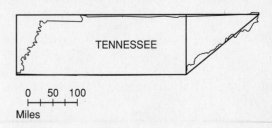

Name _____

1. Draw a time line that represents the year each war or conflict began.

   Major Wars and Conflicts of the United States (Source: Universal Almanac)

French and Indian War	1689-1697	World War I	1917-1918
Revolutionary War	1775-1783	World War II	1941-1946
War of 1812	1812-1815	Korean War	1950-1953
Mexican War	1846-1848	Vietnam War	1964-1973
Civil War	1861-1865	Desert Storm	1990-1991
Spanish American War	1898		

In Exercises 2–5 use the picture graph below. The graph shows the top five longest-running national network series of all time and the number of seasons that they aired as of 1994. (Source: Universal Almanac)

Top Five Longest Running Network Series

Program	Number of Seasons
Walt Disney	▭▯ ▭▯ ▭▯ ▭▯ ▭▯ ▭▯ ▭
60 Minutes	▭▯ ▭▯ ▭▯ ▭▯ ▭▯
The Ed Sullivan Show	▭▯ ▭▯ ▭▯ ▭▯ ▭▯
Gunsmoke	▭▯ ▭▯ ▭▯ ▭▯
The Red Skelton Show	▭▯ ▭▯ ▭▯ ▭▯ ▭▯ = 5 seasons

2. How many seasons does one TV represent?

3. Estimate the number of seasons "Walt Disney" aired.

4. How many more seasons did "60 Minutes" air than "Gunsmoke"?

5. If one TV represented 10 seasons, how would the picture graph change?

In Exercises 6–9, use the time line. The time line gives a brief history of the major advances in chemistry.

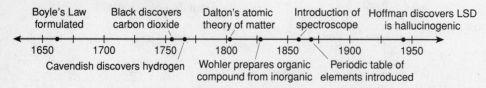

6. What is the time increment used in the time line?

7. Estimate the year Dalton's theory of matter was introduced.

8. What advance occurred in 1869?

9. Name one advance that occurred in the 17th century.

In Exercises 1 and 2, which type of bar graph do you think would best represent the data. Explain.

Number of correct answers	Number of men who scored that number	Number of women who scored that number
55-60	5	6
50-54	12	11
45-49	14	16
40-44	12	7
35-39	8	4
30-34	1	3
25-29	0	1
20-24	0	0
15-19	0	0
10-14	0	0
5-9	0	0
0-4	0	0

1. In a survey, 100 people were asked to state their blood type: 38 said A+, 3 said A-, 10 said B+, 1 said B-, 1 said AB-, 2 said AB+, 35 said O+, 3 said O-, and 7 did not know.

2. One hundred people, fifty men and fifty women, were given a timed quiz. There were 60 arithmetic problems to answer in 60 seconds. The table at the right shows the number of correct answers and the number of men and women who scored that number.

In Exercises 3–6, use the histogram which represents the total number of U.S. immigrants by decade.

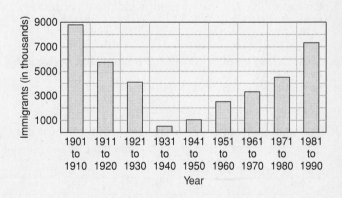

3. Which decade shows the largest number of immigrants?

4. Between which two decades did the number of immigrants decrease the most?

5. Do you see a trend in the bar graph?

6. Make an estimate of the number of immigrants from 1991-2000 base on the data in the bar graph.

7. The following are the times in seconds for 20 eighth grade students running a 40 yard dash. Show how this data can be organized by a histogram.

5.8	6.3	7.4	4.9	5.5
6.2	5.1	5.8	5.6	4.7
6.5	6.8	6.2	5.9	5.4
5.8	7.3	6.7	6.9	5.1

In Exercises 1–4, use the line graph. (Source: Universal Almanac)

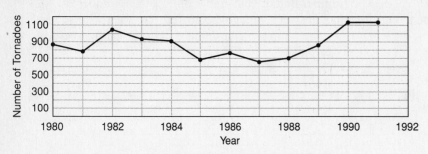

1. Name the units of the horizontal and vertical axes.
2. Estimate the total number of tornadoes in 1982.
3. During what years did the number of tornadoes decrease?
4. Why do you think the number of tornadoes seems to have increased over the last three years?

In Exercises 5 and 6, use the rectangles shown below. The width is given along the vertical side and the length is given along the horizontal side.

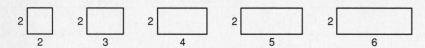

5. Create a table that lists length, width, and perimeter of each rectangle.

6. Make a line graph showing the relationship between the length and the perimeter.

7. The total national expenditures for health care for the U.S. is given in the table. Construct a line graph for this data. (Source: Universal Almanac)

Year	1960	1965	1970	1975	1980	1985	1990
Amount (in billions)	27.1	41.6	74.4	132.9	250.1	422.6	675.0

8. Write a paragraph describing a real-life situation that could represent the line graph at the right. Include the units of measure for the data, and explain how the graph can be used to answer questions about the data.

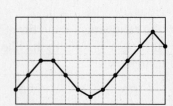

5.4

Name _____

1. The following data lists the places of origin and the number of travelers (in millions) to the U.S. in 1991. Choose a type of graph that best represents the data. Explain why you choose that type and then draw the graph. (Source: U.S. Travel and Tourism Administration)

Country	Number of travelers
Canada	18.9
Europe	7.4
Mexico	7.0
Latin America	2.0
Other	6.8

2. The graph shows the number of participants (in millions) over the age of seven that took part in popular sport activities in the U.S. in 1990.

   (Source: National Sporting Goods Association)

   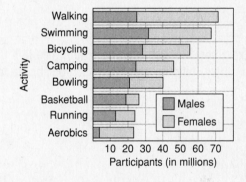

   a. Estimate the number of females who participated in basketball.

   b. In which activities are the number of females greater than the number of males?

   c. In which activity is the greatest number of people participating?

   d. Could another type of graph represent the data just as well? If so, which type?

3. Only eleven players have won Major League Baseball's Triple Crown. That is, in one season, they have lead their league in homeruns and runs batted in (RBI's), and have had the highest batting average. The table lists the players and the years when they won the Triple Crown. Draw a graph that best represents this data.

Player	Year	Player	Year
Ty Cobb	1909	Joe Medwick	1937
Heinie Zimmerman	1912	Ted Williams	1942
Rogers Hornsby	1922	Ted Williams	1947
Rogers Hornsby	1925	Mickey Mantle	1956
Chuck Klein	1933	Frank Robinson	1966
Jimmie Foxx	1933	Carl Yastrzemski	1967
Lou Gehrig	1934		

In Exercises 1–4, use the bar graph. The graph shows the per capita consumption (in pounds) of selected meats in 1990. (Source: U.S. Department of Agriculture)

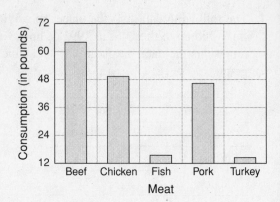

1. Judging only from the length of the bars, compare the consumption of pork to that of fish.

2. Use the scale to determine the answer in Exercise 1.

3. Is this graph misleading? Explain.

4. Use the information in the graph to create another bar graph that is not misleading.

In Exercises 5–8, use the line graph. The line graph shows the monthly bills for electricity for your home for one year.

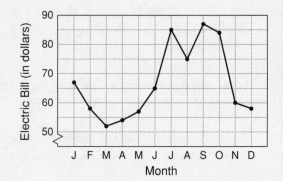

5. Without looking at the vertical scale, compare June's electrical bill to that of July.

6. Use the scale to determine the answer to Exercise 5.

7. Explain why this graph is misleading.

8. Use the information in this line graph to create another line graph that is not misleading.

5.6

Name _____

In Exercises 1 and 2, decide whether the data could have been organized
with a line plot. Explain your reasoning.

1. The following data shows the number of
games played in the Stanley Cup Finals from
1917-1993. (Source: Universal Almanac)

Games played	Years occured
2	5
3	2
4	22
5	24
6	14
7	9

2. The following data shows the number of seeds
of a particular plant that germinated within a
specified number of weeks.

Week	Number of seeds
1	6
2	9
3	13
4	16
5	7
6	2

3. The following data shows the resulting sum when a pair of six-sided dice
is tossed 100 times. Organize the data in a line plot.

```
8   4   3   5   6   7   5   7   7   7
8   6   7   8   4   8   8   4   9  10
7   9   5   7   5   9  10   6   2   7
2   8   7   9   7   9   4   9   7   6
5  10   6   4  10   9   7  10   6   9
6   9   8   7   2  10   9   7   5  11
8   3   5   9  10   5   3  10   9   3
7   6  10   4   6   7   8   6  12   5
9   4   8   8  11   8  12  11  12  11
7  10  11   6   5  12   4   6   4   8
```

4. A baseball fan examined the records of a favorite baseball
player's performance during his last 50 games. The
number of games in which the player had 0, 1, 2, 3 and
4 hits are recorded in the line plot.

a. Determine the average number of hits per game.

b. Determine the player's batting average if he had 200
at bats during the 50 game series. (batting average =
number of hits ÷ number of at bats)

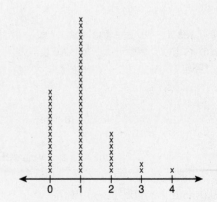

In Exercises 1–3, what type of correlation does the scatter plot have?
Describe a real-life situation that could be represented by the scatter plot.

1.
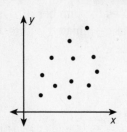

2.
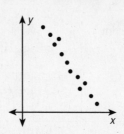

3.
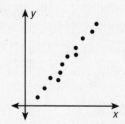

In Exercises 4–6, decide whether a scatter plot relating the two quantities
would tend to have a positive, negative, or no correlation. Explain.

4. The number of study hours and test scores

5. The number of pets you own and your age

6. The number of hours you watch TV and your test scores

In Exercises 7–10, use the data in the table. The table compares h, the
altitude in thousands of feet, and v, the speed of sound in feet per second.

h	0	5	10	15	20	25	30	35
v	1116	1097	1077	1057	1036	1015	995	973

7. Sketch a scatter plot of the data.

8. How are h and v related?

9. Estimate the speed of sound at 12,500 feet.

10. Estimate the altitude at which the speed of sound is 1000 feet/second.

In Exercises 11–13, use the scatter plot at the right. The scatter
plot shows the pre-primary school enrollment (in millions) for
years 1985 through 1991 where $t = 5$ corresponds to 1985.

(Source: U.S. Bureau of Census)

11. What was the enrollment in 1987?

12. How is the enrollment and the year related? Explain.

13. Estimate the enrollment in the year 1995.

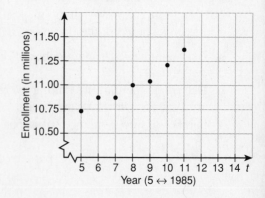

In Exercises 1–4, find the probability of rolling the following number or numbers on a die.

1. A six
2. An even number
3. A one or two
4. A number greater than two

In Exercises 5 and 6, consider the following. Six marbles are placed in a bag. One is green, two are yellow, and three are red. Without looking, choose one.

5. What is the probability of choosing a red marble?

6. What is the probability of choosing a yellow marble?

In Exercises 7–10, consider the probability of choosing one card from a standard deck of 52 playing cards. (A face card is a Jack, Queen, or King.)

7. What is the probability of choosing an "8"?

8. What is the probability of choosing a face card?

9. What is the probability of choosing a red face card?

10. What is the probability of choosing a "2" or an Ace?

11. 20 socks are placed in a laundry bag. Use the following statements to determine the number of socks of a particular color.
    - Probability of blue is 0.25.
    - Probability of white is 0.50.
    - Probability of black is 0.20.
    - Probability of argyle is 0.05.

In Exercises 12–14, use the following information. The number of colleges and universities in the United States in 1987 is shown by region in the figure. (Source: U.S. National Center for Education Statistics)

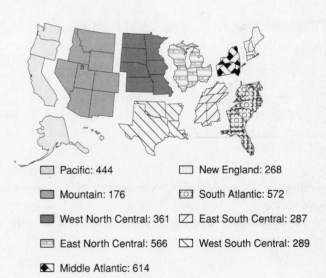

Pacific: 444
New England: 268
Mountain: 176
South Atlantic: 572
West North Central: 361
East South Central: 287
East North Central: 566
West South Central: 289
Middle Atlantic: 614

12. Suppose one institution is selected at random. What is the probability that the institution is in the
    a. Middle Atlantic Region?
    b. Pacific Region?

13. What is the probability that one institution selected at random is in one of three southern regions?

14. Using only the result from Exercise 13, what is the probability that one university selected at random is *not* in one of the three southern regions?

6.1

Name _____

In Exercises 1–6, use the divisibility tests to determine whether the number is divisible by 2, 3, 4, 5, 6, 7, 8, 9, and 10.

1. 384

2. 945

3. 51,840

4. 2232

5. 7614

6. 21,735

7. Which digits will make the number 34, ? 21 divisible by 9?

8. Which digits will make the number 21,7 ? 6 divisible by 4?

9. Which digits will make the number 3,204, ? 62 divisible by 3?

10. Which digits will make the number 24 ? divisible by 6?

11. Which digits will make the number 7 ? 5 divisible by 5?

12. Find the smallest natural number divisible by 3, 5, 7, and 9.

13. Find the smallest natural number divisible by 2, 4, 6, and 8.

14. If the numbers a and b are both divisible by 4, which of the following must also be divisible by 4. Explain your reasoning.

   a. $a + b$ b. $a - b$ c. ab d. $\dfrac{a}{b}$

In Exercises 15–18, find all factors of the number.

15. 24

16. 54

17. 48

18. 105

19. A rectangular region of state forest land has an area of 80 square miles. The length and the width are natural numbers. Find the possible dimensions.

20. A rancher wants to fence in a corral for his prize winning stallion. He wishes to have an area of 400 square yards. He also wants the perimeter to be as small as possible in order to minimize the cost of the fencing. If the side lengths are natural numbers, find the dimensions of the corral.

Extra Practice

6.2

Name _____

In Exercises 1–3, is the number prime or composite? Explain.

1. 39

2. 41

3. 57

In Exercises 4–6, write the factorization represented by the tree diagram. Write your answer in exponent form.

4.

5.

6.

In Exercises 7–12, write the prime factorization of the number. Write your answer in exponent form.

7. 42

8. 64

9. 84

10. 144

11. 200

12. 180

In Exercises 13–16, write the expression in expanded form and exponent form.

13. -36

14. -45

15. $24x^2$

16. $16a^3b^2$

In Exercises 17–19, evaluate the expression.

17. $3^2 \cdot 2 \cdot 5$

18. $2^4 \cdot 3 \cdot 7$

19. $-1 \cdot 3^3 \cdot 2^2 \cdot 5$

In Exercises 20–22, list all possible factors of the number.

20. 16

21. 24

22. 54

23. One of the theorems of Pierre de Fermat states that every prime number that can be written as a sum of $4n$ and 1, where n is a natural number, can also be written as the sum of two square numbers. For example, when $n = 7$, $29 = 4(7) + 1$ is prime and $29 = 25 + 4$, where 25 and 4 are square numbers. Write the primes less than 100 that can be written as $4n + 1$, where n is a natural number. Then, express each of these primes as the sum of two square numbers.

24. The prime numbers 2 and 3 are consecutive numbers. Can you think of any other pairs of consecutive primes. Explain.

Extra Practice 6.3

Name _____

In Exercises 1–6, find the greatest common factor of the numbers.

1. 12, 30   **2.** 48, 54   **3.** 60, 130

4. 108, 198   **5.** 720, 1200   **6.** 660, 1155

In Exercises 7–10, find the greatest common factor of the expressions.

7. $2x^2y$, $10xy^2$ **8.** $4x^2y^3$, $18xy^2$

9. $5r^2p^3$, $20r^3p$ **10.** $36x^2y^3$, $63x^2y^4$

In Exercises 11–13, find two pairs of numbers that have the given greatest common factor. (There are many correct answers.)

11. 5   **12.** 3   **13.** 12

In Exercises 14–16, decide whether the numbers are relatively prime.

14. 256 and 315   **15.** 321 and 405   **16.** 190 and 343

In Exercises 17–19, find the area and perimeter of the rectangle. Are the two measures relatively prime? Explain.

17.   **18.**   **19.**

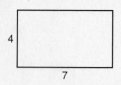

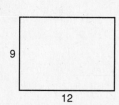

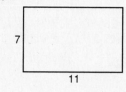

20. Find the greatest common factor of the terms in the following sequence:
2, 6, 10, 14, 18, . . .

21. Find the greatest common factor of the terms in the following sequence:
3, 9, 15, 21, 27, . . .

22. A group of children walk to the corner store and buy cans of soda pop for a total of $3.36 and candy bars for a total of $2.45. Each child has one can of pop and one candy bar. How many children were in the group? What is the cost of one can of soda and one candy bar?

In Exercises 1–6, list the first several multiple of each number. Use the list to find the least common multiple.

1. 5, 7

2. 3, 8

3. 9, 12

4. 12, 14

5. 3, 5, 6

6. 5, 6, 12

In Exercises 7–12, write the prime factorization of each expression. Use the result to find the least common multiple.

7. 36, 54

8. 15, 35

9. 145, 275

10. 81, 216

11. $13xy^2, 26x^2y^3$

12. $3x^2, 5y^2$

In Exercises 13–16, find a pair of numbers that satisfy the conditions.

13. Two prime numbers whose LCM is 39.

14. Two composite numbers whose LCM is 36.

15. Two square numbers whose LCM is 100.

16. Two even numbers whose LCM is 72.

17. You have collected empty pop bottles to return for a 8¢ per bottle refund. You want to use the money to buy packs of trading cards for $1.50 per pack. After buying the packs you had no money left over. What is the fewest number of pop bottles you could have returned? How many packs of cards did you buy?

18. Angel's car gets 32 miles per gallon and Mo's car gets 22 miles per gallon. When traveling from Morgan Run to Clinton, they both used a whole number of gallons of gasoline. What is the closest that Morgan Run and Clinton could be? How many gallons did Angel's car use? How many gallons did Mo's car use?

19. Mr. Wilson has a problem. He can't sleep when the dogs in his neighborhood start howling at the full moon. Luckily, it takes the sound of two dogs barking at the same time to awake him. Last night, Sparky started barking at 1:00 A.M. and barked every 12 minutes. Trigger also started at 1:00 A.M. and barked every 14 minutes. After Mr. Wilson fell back to sleep, he woke up again when Sparky and Trigger barked simultaneously. What time was it?

In Exercises 1–6, what is the greatest common factor of the numerator and denominator? Use your answer to simplify the fraction.

1. $\frac{12}{28}$

2. $\frac{8}{36}$

3. $\frac{9}{45}$

4. $\frac{22}{77}$

5. $\frac{4}{38}$

6. $\frac{84}{108}$

In Exercises 7–12, simplify the variable expression.

7. $\frac{2xy}{6xy^2}$

8. $\frac{3ab}{12a^2}$

9. $\frac{49z^2}{147z^5}$

10. $\frac{16yz^2}{18z}$

11. $\frac{24x^3y}{40xy^5}$

12. $\frac{38x^2}{95xy^2}$

In Exercises 13–16, determine which of the fractions are not equivalent to the given fraction.

13. $\frac{3}{4}$: $\frac{18}{24}, \frac{21}{28}, \frac{15}{20}, \frac{9}{16}$

14. $\frac{2}{7}$: $\frac{4}{14}, \frac{6}{21}, \frac{7}{12}, \frac{4}{49}$

15. $\frac{3}{8}$: $\frac{6}{16}, \frac{9}{24}, \frac{9}{64}, \frac{15}{20}$

16. $\frac{5}{8}$: $\frac{15}{24}, \frac{25}{64}, \frac{10}{16}, \frac{45}{72}$

In Exercises 17–19, write 3 fractions that are equivalent to the given fraction.

17. $\frac{4}{5}$

18. $\frac{7}{8}$

19. $\frac{11}{33}$

In Exercises 20–25, complete the statement with $<$, $>$, or $=$.

20. $\frac{1}{6}$ ☐ $\frac{1}{9}$

21. $\frac{22}{24}$ ☐ $\frac{33}{36}$

22. $\frac{1}{10}$ ☐ $\frac{3}{18}$

23. $\frac{6}{9}$ ☐ $\frac{8}{12}$

24. $\frac{26}{39}$ ☐ $\frac{5}{8}$

25. $\frac{15}{18}$ ☐ $\frac{65}{78}$

In Exercises 26 and 27, use the table which shows the number of miles ridden per day during a 7 day bike trip from the town of Osceola to the town of Fairview.

Day	1	2	3	4	5	6	7
Number of miles	20	30	30	40	30	40	30

26. Express the number of miles ridden on day 1 as a fraction of the total miles.

27. Express the number of miles ridden on day 6 as a fraction of the total miles.

28. Miss Curtis and Mr. Morgan gave the same test to their eighth grade math classes. In Miss Curtis' class, 21 out of 35 students received a grade of B or higher. In Mr. Morgan's class, 24 out of 36 students received a grade of B or higher. Which class did better? Explain.

6.6

Name _____

In Exercises 1–6, write the number as a fraction in simplest form.

1. -3

2. 0.55

3. 0.36

4. $10\frac{2}{3}$

5. $-3\frac{2}{5}$

6. $16\frac{3}{4}$

In Exercises 7–12, decide whether the number is rational or irrational. Then write the decimal form of the number and state whether the decimal is terminating, repeating, or nonrepeating.

7. $\frac{4}{11}$

8. $\frac{5}{8}$

9. $\sqrt{16}$

10. $\sqrt{32}$

11. $\frac{9}{16}$

12. $\frac{8}{25}$

In Exercises 13–18, write the decimal as a fraction. Simplify the result.

13. 0.7

14. 0.52

15. 0.95

16. 0.22

17. $0.\overline{94}$

18. $4.\overline{2}$

In Exercises 19–22, match the rational number with its decimal form.

a. $0.\overline{23}$ **b.** 3.15 **c.** 0.65 **d.** $0.0\overline{21}$

19. $3\frac{3}{20}$

20. $\frac{23}{99}$

21. $\frac{7}{330}$

22. $\frac{13}{20}$

23. Write each rational number in decimal form. Then describe the pattern.
$\frac{1}{9}, \frac{2}{9}, \frac{3}{9}, \frac{4}{9}, \frac{5}{9}, \frac{6}{9}$

In Exercises 24 and 25, find the perimeter of the figure. Write the result in three ways: in fraction form, as a mixed number, and as a decimal.

24.

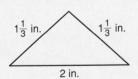

$1\frac{1}{3}$ in. $1\frac{1}{3}$ in.

2 in.

25.

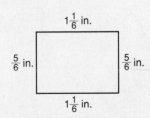

$1\frac{1}{6}$ in.

$\frac{5}{6}$ in. $\frac{5}{6}$ in.

$1\frac{1}{6}$ in.

26. A group of students participated in a 100 hour rock-a-thon to raise money for a local charity. The table shows the portion of the fund-raiser in which each student was involved. Write each fraction in decimal form. Then order the students from the one which did the most rocking to the least.

Student	Ken	Vicki	Cindy	Jose	Brenda	Doug	JiLynn
Number	$\frac{1}{5}$	$\frac{4}{25}$	$\frac{3}{25}$	$\frac{11}{50}$	$\frac{1}{10}$	$\frac{3}{20}$	$\frac{1}{20}$

Name _____

In Exercises 1–6, simplify the expression.

1. 4^{-2} 2. -3^{-3} 3. 5^0

4. $(-3)^2$ 5. $3x^{-2}$ 6. $(4x)^{-2}$

In Exercises 7–12, simplify the expression.

7. $(-3)^2 \cdot (-3)^{-4}$ 8. $14^0 \cdot 14^{-1}$ 9. $x^{-15} \cdot x^{20}$

10. $\dfrac{3^5}{3^{-2}}$ 11. $\dfrac{-8^3}{-8^2}$ 12. $\dfrac{x^0}{x^{-3}}$

In Exercises 13–15, use a calculator to evaluate the expression. If necessary, round the result to 3 decimal places.

13. 6.8^5 14. $86^{-3} \cdot 86^5$ 15. $\dfrac{0.25^{-2}}{0.25^3}$

In Exercises 16–18, solve the equation for n.

16. $\dfrac{4^7}{4^3} = 4^n$ 17. $3.5^n = 1$ 18. $4^{-n} \cdot 4^{-6} = 4^8$

In Exercises 19–21, find the largest value of n so that the inequality is true.

19. $5^n < 100,000$ 20. $2^{-n} > 0.001$ 21. $50^n < 1,000,000$

In Exercises 22 and 23, write an expression for the verbal phrase.

22. The product of eight raised to the negative fifth power and eight raised to the seventh power.

23. The quotient of five raised to sixth power and five raised to the negative fourth power.

In Exercises 24–26, complete the statement with $<$, $>$, or $=$.

24. 6^{-2} ☐ 2^{-6} 25. 10^0 ☐ 0^{10} 26. $\dfrac{5^2}{5^{-3}}$ ☐ $\dfrac{5^{-3}}{5^2}$

27. The lengths of the sides of a rectangle are 5^3 yards and 5^2 yards. Write the area of the rectangle as a power of 5.

28. \$3000 is deposited in an account earning 8% compounded annually. Calculate the amount in the account after four years by using the equation $C = 3000(1.08)^4$.

In Exercises 1–6, write the number in scientific notation.

1. 3500   **2.** 62,000   **3.** 0.000375

4. 0.0205   **5.** 62,153,000   **6.** 0.0000105

In Exercises 7–12, write the number in decimal form.

7. 3.2×10^5 **8.** 6.35×10^{-4} **9.** 4.3×10^{-3}

10. 9.75×10^4 **11.** 8.27×10^{-6} **12.** 3.25×10^5

In Exercises 13–18, decide whether the number is in scientific notation. If it is not, rewrite the number in scientific notation.

13. 2.5×10^6 **14.** 0.35×10^6 **15.** 26.5×10^{-3}

16. 3.2×10^{-6} **17.** 764×10^{-3} **18.** 5.25×10^{-1}

In Exercises 19–22, evaluate the product. Write the result in scientific notation and in decimal form.

19. $(3.2 \times 10^5)(4 \times 10^2)$ **20.** $(3.0 \times 10^7)(6.5 \times 10^{-2})$

21. $(5.2 \times 10^{-4})(7.2 \times 10^{-6})$ **22.** $(9.5 \times 10^3)(2.3 \times 10^{-7})$

In Exercises 23 and 24, decide which is larger. Explain.

23. 1×10^6 or 6×10^5 **24.** 1×10^{-4} or 4×10^{-3}

25. The star Beta Andromeda is approximately 76 light years from Earth. Estimate the distance to this star if a light year is approximately 5.88×10^{12} miles. Write your estimate in scientific notation.

26. The hydraulic cylinder in a large press contains 2 gallons of oil. When the cylinder is under full pressure the actual volume of oil will decrease by $2(150)(2.0 \times 10^{-5})$ gallons. Write this decrease in decimal and scientific notation. What is the actual volume when the cylinder is under full pressure?

In Exercises 1 and 2, use the formula to construct a table similar to that shown in Exercise 2 on page 281 of the textbook.

1. $n^2 - n$

2. $n^2 + 2$

In Exercises 3 and 4, describe the pattern. Then list the next three terms.

3. $1, \frac{1}{2}, \frac{1}{3}, \frac{1}{4}, \ldots$

4. $\frac{1}{2}, \frac{1}{5}, \frac{1}{10}, \frac{1}{17}, \frac{1}{26} \ldots$

5. The sequence 1, 1, 3, 5, 9, 15, 25, ... is similar to the Fibonacci sequence. Describe the pattern. Then list the next three terms.

In Exercises 6 and 7, each figure represents a figurate number. Predict the next two numbers in the sequence. Then draw figures to check your solutions.

6.

  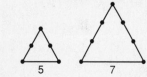

7.

8. Find two pairs of symmetric primes of 20.

9. Find two pairs of symmetric primes of 15.

In Exercises 10 and 11, use the following figure. It is called the von Koch snowflake, an example from a new area of mathematics called fractal geometry.

Star 1   Star 2   Star 3

10. Describe the pattern.

11. Count the number of points in each star.

12. Two numbers are said to be betrothed if the sum of all the factors, other than 1 and itself, of one number equals the other. For example:
The factors of 195 except for 1 and 195 are 3, 5, 13, 15, 39, 65.
The factors of 140 except for 1 and 140 are 2, 4, 5, 7, 10, 14, 20, 28, 35, 70.
$$195 = 2 + 4 + 5 + 7 + 10 + 14 + 20 + 28 + 35 + 70$$
$$140 = 3 + 5 + 13 + 15 + 39 + 65$$
Now prove that 48 and 75 are betrothed.

7.1

Name _____

In Exercises 1–6, add or subtract. Then simplify, if possible.

1. $\dfrac{3}{7} + \dfrac{2}{7}$

2. $\dfrac{6}{12} - \dfrac{3}{12}$

3. $\dfrac{-7}{15} + \dfrac{2}{15}$

4. $\dfrac{6}{10} - \dfrac{2}{10}$

5. $-\dfrac{8}{3} + -\dfrac{11}{3}$

6. $3\dfrac{1}{3} + 4\dfrac{1}{3}$

In Exercises 7–12, add or subtract. Then simplify, if possible.

7. $\dfrac{x}{4} + \dfrac{2x}{4}$

8. $\dfrac{3z}{7} - \dfrac{4z}{7}$

9. $\dfrac{-c}{10} + \dfrac{-19c}{10}$

10. $\dfrac{6}{x} - \dfrac{10}{x}$

11. $\dfrac{6}{3z} + \dfrac{12}{3z}$

12. $\dfrac{-16}{10k} - \dfrac{22}{10k}$

In Exercises 13–18, solve the equation. Then simplify, if possible.

13. $t + \dfrac{3}{4} = -\dfrac{6}{4}$

14. $q - \dfrac{2}{3} = \dfrac{7}{3}$

15. $p + \dfrac{18}{7} = \dfrac{11}{7}$

16. $s + \dfrac{4}{9} = -\dfrac{14}{9}$

17. $w - \dfrac{4}{9} = -\dfrac{19}{9}$

18. $2x + \dfrac{1}{4} = -\dfrac{7}{4}$

In Exercises 19–21, use a calculator to evaluate the expression as a decimal rounded to two decimal places.

19. $\dfrac{3}{6} + \dfrac{1}{6}$

20. $-\dfrac{9}{11} + \dfrac{4}{11}$

21. $\dfrac{5}{16} - \dfrac{19}{16}$

In Exercises 22 and 23, add or subtract. Then describe the pattern and write the next three numbers in the pattern.

22. $\dfrac{1}{6} + \dfrac{2}{6} = \boxed{?}$

   $\dfrac{2}{6} + \dfrac{3}{6} = \boxed{?}$

   $\dfrac{3}{6} + \dfrac{4}{6} = \boxed{?}$

23. $\dfrac{12}{3} - \dfrac{1}{3} = \boxed{?}$

   $-\dfrac{11}{3} + \dfrac{2}{3} = \boxed{?}$

   $\dfrac{10}{3} - \dfrac{3}{3} = \boxed{?}$

In Exercises 24 and 25, write the indicated sum or difference.

24.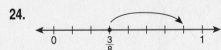

25.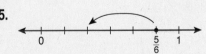

26. You are helping to wallpaper your room. You find that for the border you need lengths of 12 ft $10\dfrac{1}{8}$ in., 10 ft $6\dfrac{3}{8}$ in., 9 ft $5\dfrac{5}{8}$ in., and 9 ft $3\dfrac{7}{8}$ in. What total length (in inches) of border do you need?

27. Suppose on Monday you bought 50 shares of stock at $\$48\dfrac{1}{8}$ per share. During the week the stocks rose and fell as shown in the table.

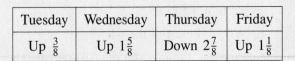

Tuesday	Wednesday	Thursday	Friday
Up $\dfrac{3}{8}$	Up $1\dfrac{5}{8}$	Down $2\dfrac{7}{8}$	Up $1\dfrac{1}{8}$

   a. What was the value of the stock on Tuesday?

   b. What was the value of the stock on Wednesday?

   c. What was the value of the stock at the end of the week?

In Exercises 1–6, find the sum or difference. Then simplify, if possible.

1. $\frac{1}{3} + \frac{5}{12}$

2. $\frac{6}{7} - \frac{11}{14}$

3. $-\frac{1}{8} + -\frac{7}{16}$

4. $\frac{1}{3} + \frac{3}{8}$

5. $-\frac{5}{6} + \frac{1}{9}$

6. $\frac{7}{10} + -\frac{2}{3}$

In Exercises 7–12, find the sum or difference. Then simplify, if possible.

7. $\frac{x}{4} + \frac{3x}{8}$

8. $\frac{a}{3} - \frac{11a}{12}$

9. $\frac{3}{y} + \frac{6}{5}$

10. $-\frac{6}{7t} + \frac{3}{14t}$

11. $\frac{5}{a} - \frac{2}{b}$

12. $\frac{7}{mn} + \frac{2}{3m}$

In Exercises 13–15, use a calculator to find the sum or difference as a decimal rounded to two decimal places.

13. $\frac{11}{16} - \frac{3}{4}$

14. $\frac{6}{25} + \frac{7}{15}$

15. $-\frac{13}{144} + \frac{11}{16}$

In Exercises 16 and 17, find the perimeter of the figure.

16.

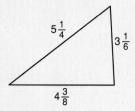

17.

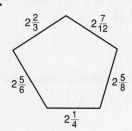

In Exercises 18 and 19, find the unknown fractional part of the pie chart. Remember that the sum of all the fractional parts is 1.

18.

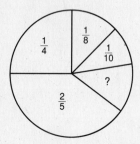

19.

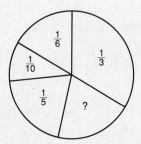

20. Four friends are working together to paint a barn for one of their uncles. The table gives the fractional part of the job done by each of the four:

   a. Who did most of the work?

   b. Find the difference in the portions done by Hank and Betsy.

   c. Find the portion of the work done by Carl and Maureen.

   d. Show that the sum of the four fractions is 1.

Maureen	$\frac{1}{6}$
Hank	$\frac{3}{8}$
Betsy	$\frac{5}{24}$
Carl	$\frac{1}{4}$

In Exercises 1–6, evaluate the expression.

1. $0.25 + 0.71$

2. $1.725 - 1.032$

3. $5.79 + 3.26$

4. $1.26 - 2.65$

5. $4.253 + 3.624$

6. $-0.021 + 4.268$

In Exercises 7 and 8, write the expression represented by the model. Then evaluate the expression by first converting to decimals. Round your result to two decimal places.

7.

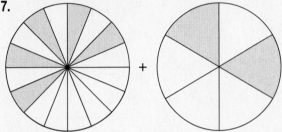

8.

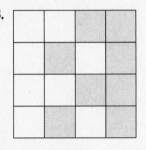

In Exercises 9–11, sketch a geometric model of the fraction. (Use a different model for each exercise.)

9. $\frac{3}{8}$

10. $\frac{19}{36}$

11. 0.72

In Exercises 12–17, evaluate the expression by first rewriting in decimal form. Round your answer to two decimal places.

12. $\frac{71}{105} - \frac{62}{99}$

13. $\frac{25}{31}m + \frac{16}{35}m$

14. $2 - \left(\frac{33}{47} + \frac{16}{19} + \frac{6}{25}\right)$

15. $5x - \left(\frac{4}{7}x + \frac{6}{11}x\right)$

16. $5\frac{1}{4} + 3\frac{2}{9} - 2\frac{6}{11}$

17. $4x - \left(\frac{5}{9}x - \frac{4}{3}x\right)$

In Exercises 18–20, use the circle graph, which shows electricity sources for the United States. (Source: Department of Energy)

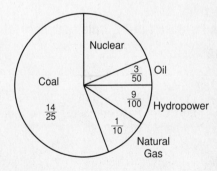

18. Find the sum of the portions for all sources other than nuclear.

19. What portion was supplied by nuclear power?

20. Find the portion supplied by nuclear power and coal.

21. Shown are two solutions to the calculation of $-\frac{11}{17} + \frac{23}{29}$. The solution is to be rounded to two decimal places. Which of the two solutions is more accurate? Explain.

a. $-\frac{11}{17} + \frac{23}{29} \approx -0.647 + 0.793$
$= 0.15$

b. $-\frac{11}{17} + \frac{23}{29} \approx -0.65 + 0.79$
$= 0.14$

7.4

Name _____

In Exercises 1–6, multiply. Then simplify, if possible.

1. $\frac{1}{8} \cdot \frac{8}{9}$

2. $-\frac{3}{7} \cdot \frac{21}{25}$

3. $-\frac{7}{8} \cdot \frac{14}{17}$

4. $3\frac{1}{4} \cdot \left(-5\frac{3}{5}\right)$

5. $-3\frac{1}{7} \cdot \left(-1\frac{1}{2}\right)$

6. $\frac{3}{8} \cdot \frac{-13}{15} \cdot \frac{16}{39}$

In Exercises 7–12, multiply. Then simplify, if possible.

7. $\frac{3x}{4} \cdot 8$

8. $16 \cdot \frac{7y}{2}$

9. $-\frac{7x}{9} \cdot \frac{3}{14x}$

10. $-\frac{17t}{20} \cdot \frac{24}{51t}$

11. $-\frac{7}{8} \cdot \left(\frac{-24z}{35}\right)$

12. $-\frac{32x^2}{9} \cdot \frac{18}{4x}$

In Exercises 13–15, find the area of the figure.

13.

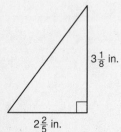

$3\frac{1}{8}$ in.

$2\frac{2}{5}$ in.

14.

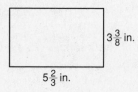

$3\frac{3}{8}$ in.

$5\frac{2}{3}$ in.

15.

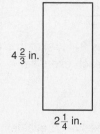

$4\frac{2}{3}$ in.

$2\frac{1}{4}$ in.

In Exercises 16–18, use a calculator to multiply the fractions. Round your result to three decimal places.

16. $\frac{8}{11} \cdot \frac{3}{4}$

17. $\frac{19}{22} \cdot 3\frac{2}{3}$

18. $\frac{29}{32} \cdot (-6)$

In Exercises 19–21, write each decimal as a fraction. Then multiply.

19. $0.3 \cdot 0.9$

20. $0.75 \cdot 0.2$

21. $0.375 \cdot 0.6$

22. A farmer wants to plow his land. He owns $7\frac{3}{4}$ acres. It takes about $2\frac{2}{3}$ hours to plow one acre. How long will it take for the farmer to plow his entire farmland?

23. Two hundred shares of stock are purchased at a price of $\$23\frac{5}{8}$ per share and three hundred shares of stock are purchased at $\$86\frac{1}{4}$ per share. Find the total cost of the purchased stock.

Name _____

In Exercises 1–6, write the reciprocal.

1. $\dfrac{1}{5}$

2. $\dfrac{7}{y}$

3. $\dfrac{3z}{4}$

4. $-7\dfrac{1}{4}$

5. $16x$

6. $-\dfrac{1}{8m}$

In Exercises 7 and 8, describe the error. Then correct it.

7.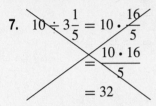

8.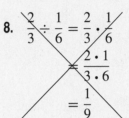

In Exercises 9–14, simplify the expression.

9. $\frac{3}{8} \div 2$

10. $\frac{3}{8} \div 3$

11. $\frac{3}{8} \div 4$

12. $\frac{5}{6} \div 2$

13. $\frac{5}{6} \div 3$

14. $\frac{5}{6} \div 4$

In Exercises 15–20, simplify the expression.

15. $\frac{3}{8} \div \frac{1}{2}$

16. $\frac{3}{8} \div \frac{1}{3}$

17. $\frac{3}{8} \div \frac{1}{4}$

18. $\frac{5}{6} \div \frac{1}{2}$

19. $\frac{5}{6} \div \frac{1}{3}$

20. $\frac{5}{6} \div \frac{1}{4}$

In Exercises 21–26, simplify the expression.

21. $\frac{3}{7} \div \frac{5}{14}$

22. $6 \div -\frac{7}{12}$

23. $-\frac{3}{4} \div \frac{3}{7}$

24. $\dfrac{16x}{21} \div \dfrac{27x}{12}$

25. $3\frac{4}{5} \div z$

26. $p \div 3\frac{2}{7}$

27. A giant size box of washing detergent contains 30 cups. On average, you use $\frac{3}{4}$ cup per load of laundry. How many loads of laundry can you do from this one box?

28. You're having a birthday party for your sister. Thirty people are to attend. You have purchased a 10-foot sub for the party. The sub weighs $8\frac{5}{8}$ ounces per foot. How much does the entire sub weigh? How many ounces does each person receive?

Name _____

In Exercises 1–4, determine the percent of the figure that is shaded.

1.

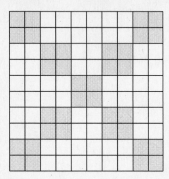

2.

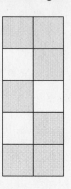

3.

4.

5. Which of the following has the least percent of its area shaded? Which has the greatest?

a.

b.

c.

d.

In Exercises 6–11, write each portion as a percent.

6. $\frac{2}{20}$

7. $\frac{24}{50}$

8. $\frac{16}{40}$

9. $\frac{39}{60}$

10. $\frac{72}{120}$

11. $\frac{196}{400}$

In Exercises 12–14, draw two geometric models for the percent.

12. 20%

13. 60%

14. 75%

In Exercises 15 and 16, the pie graph shows the monthly budget for a family of four.

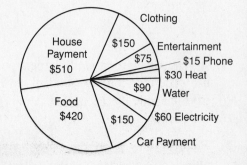

15. What is the total budget for the month?

16. Construct a table determining the percent of the budget devoted to each area.

17. Determine which figure does not fit the pattern. Explain.

a.

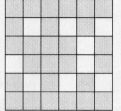

b.

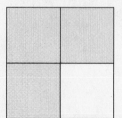

c.

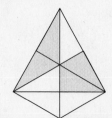

d.

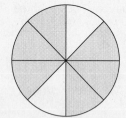

Name _____

In Exercises 1–6, rewrite the percent as a decimal.

1. 48%   2. 16%   3. 250%

4. 84.2%   5. 0.5%   6. $38\frac{2}{5}\%$

In Exercises 7–12, rewrite the decimal as a percent.

7. 0.63   8. 0.92   9. 1.65

10. 0.008   11. 0.021   12. 1.384

In Exercises 13–16, complete the statement with <, >, or =.

13. $\frac{5}{8}$? 62.5%   14. $\frac{7}{16}$? 45%

15. $\frac{7}{25}$? 2.8%   16. $\frac{9}{20}$? 0.45%

In Exercises 17–22, rewrite the percent as a fraction in simplest form.

17. 68%   18. 35%   19. 79%

20. 125%   21. 345%   22. 105%

In Exercises 23–28, rewrite the fraction as a percent.

23. $\frac{28}{32}$ 24. $\frac{39}{60}$ 25. $\frac{250}{625}$

26. $\frac{120}{32}$ 27. $\frac{99}{450}$ 28. $\frac{180}{80}$

In Exercises 29–31, what percent of the entire region is shaded?

29.   30.   31.

In Exercises 32 and 33, use the following information.

Three hundred people were surveyed and reported that they rearrange furniture in their homes for several reasons. The table shows the data.

32. Create a new table showing the percent of the people surveyed who reported each reason. Also include the percent written as a decimal and a fraction in simplest form.

Reason	Number of People
Bored with present arrangement	108
Moving to new residence	57
Purchasing new furniture	45
Redecorating	48
Other	42

33. Create a bar graph showing the results of the survey.

In Exercises 1–6, write the percent as a decimal. Then multiply to find the percent of the number.

1. 18% of 800

2. 23% of 120

3. 360% of 8

4. 175% of 40

5. 0.6% of 540

6. 3.5% of 150

In Exercises 7–10, match the percent phrase with the fraction phrase. Then find the percent of the number.

a. $\frac{1}{6}$ of 80

b. $\frac{1}{12}$ of 80

c. $\frac{1}{20}$ of 80

d. $\frac{3}{8}$ of 80

7. 5% of 80

8. 37.5% of 80

9. $16\frac{2}{3}$% of 80

10. $8\frac{1}{3}$% of 80

In Exercises 11 and 12, shade the indicated number of squares.

11.

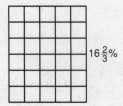
$16\frac{2}{3}$%

12.

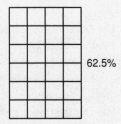
62.5%

In Exercises 13–18, use the percent key on a calculator to find the percent of the number. Round the result to 2 decimal places.

13. 74% of 55

14. 18% of 39

15. 58.2% of 340

16. 228% of 120

17. 3.05% of 690

18. 101% of 252

In Exercises 19–22, use the rectangle at the right.

19. Find the perimeter and area of the rectangle.

20. Draw a new rectangle whose dimensions are $33\frac{1}{3}$% of the given rectangle. Find the perimeter and area of the new rectangle.

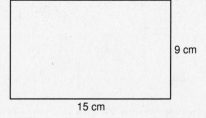
9 cm

15 cm

21. Find $33\frac{1}{3}$% of the perimeter of the given rectangle. Is the result equal to the perimeter of the new rectangle? Why or why not?

22. Find $33\frac{1}{3}$% of the area of the given rectangle. Is the result equal to the area of the new rectangle? Why or why not?

23. There is a sale at the sport store of "20% off." The original price of the new cross-trainers you want is $79.95. What is the sale price?

24. You read in the newspaper that the price of a new CD player is predicted to be 125% of this year's price. If the price of the model you wanted is $525.95, what is the predicted price for next year?

Extra Practice 7.9

In Exercises 1–3, the price of an item is given. Find the total cost of the item, including a 6% sales tax.

1. $7.95   2. $59.35   3. $135.99

In Exercises 4–15, consider the following. In 1990, the total population of the United States was 250 million people. What percent of the United States population is each state's population? Round answers to one decimal place, if necessary.

4. Alaska: 0.6 million   5. California: 30.4 million

6. Illinois: 11.5 million   7. Michigan: 9.4 million

8. Montana: 0.8 million   9. New York: 18.1 million

10. Ohio: 10.9 million   11. Pennsylvania: 12.0 million

12. South Carolina: 3.6 million   13. Texas: 17.3 million

14. Virginia: 6.3 million   15. Wyoming: 0.5 million

16. A union negotiates for a cost-of-living raise of 7%. Find the amount of the raise for a union member whose salary is $17,240. What is the new salary for this person?

17. The seating capacity of the university football stadium is to be increased by 15.5%. The current seating capacity is 68,000. What will be the new seating capacity?

18. Thirty-five percent of the students enrolled in a college are freshmen. The enrollment of college is 2800. Find the number of freshmen.

19. The price of a new van in 1990 was $20,565. The current price is 10% more than the price in 1990. What is the increase in price over the years? What is the current price of the new van?

20. Because of slumping sales, a small company laid off 30 of its 153 employees. What percent of the work force was laid off? Using your answer, what percent of the work force was retained? Using this percent, calculate the number of workers retained. Does this answer agree with the number of workers retained ($150 - 30 = 123$)? Explain.

21. During a certain winter, 120 inches of snow fell. Of that, 86 inches fell in December. What percent of snow fell in December? What percent of snow fell in months other than December?

In Exercises 1–3, determine whether the quotient is a rate or a ratio. Then simplify.

1. $\dfrac{240 \text{ feet}}{30 \text{ seconds}}$

2. $\dfrac{76 \text{ players}}{144 \text{ players}}$

3. $\dfrac{210 \text{ hits}}{165 \text{ games}}$

In Exercises 4–7, write the verbal phrase as a rate or a ratio. Then simplify. Explain why the phrase is a rate or a ratio.

4. Ran 3 miles in 24 minutes

5. 10 out of 60 students agree

6. Rained 2 inches in 40 minutes

7. Painted 2 out of 3 pictures

In Exercises 8–13, write each quotient as a ratio and simplify.

8. $\dfrac{4 \text{ yards}}{16 \text{ inches}}$

9. $\dfrac{32 \text{ km}}{4000 \text{ m}}$

10. $\dfrac{36 \text{ hours}}{7 \text{ days}}$

11. $\dfrac{7 \text{ pints}}{2 \text{ gallons}}$

12. $\dfrac{3 \text{ feet}}{28 \text{ inches}}$

13. $\dfrac{2 \text{ pounds}}{24 \text{ ounces}}$

14. A swimming pool having dimensions as shown took 48 hours to fill. Find the volume. At what rate, in cubic feet per hour, did the water flow?

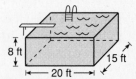

15. A family is traveling to the beach for their vacation. At 2 P.M. they stop at a gas station and fill the gas tank. You notice that the odometer reading was 36,525. At 8:30 P.M. they again stop to fill the tank. It takes about 16 gallons to fill. The odometer now reads 36,913.

    a. Determine the number of miles the car travels per gallon of gas.

    b. Determine the average rate, in miles per hour, at which you are traveling during that time period.

In Exercises 16 and 17, decide which is the better bargain. Explain your reasoning.

16. a. 2 quarts for $2.15
    b. one gallon for $4.25

17. a. 36 ounce box for $3.72
    b. 3 pound box for $5.36

In Exercises 18 and 19, find the ratio of the perimeter of the shaded figure to the perimeter of the unshaded figure. Then find the ratio of the area of the shaded figure to the area of the unshaded figure.

18.

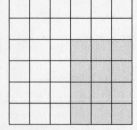

19.

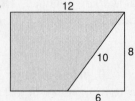

8.2

Name _____

In Exercises 1–3, decide whether the proportion is true. Explain your reasoning.

1. $\dfrac{1}{6} \overset{?}{=} \dfrac{7}{42}$

2. $\dfrac{2}{3} \overset{?}{=} \dfrac{4}{9}$

3. $\dfrac{5}{12} \overset{?}{=} \dfrac{10}{120}$

In Exercises 4–9, solve the proportion. Check your solution.

4. $\dfrac{x}{5} = \dfrac{15}{25}$

5. $\dfrac{6}{11} = \dfrac{w}{22}$

6. $\dfrac{7}{10} = \dfrac{56}{z}$

7. $\dfrac{8}{q} = \dfrac{2}{9}$

8. $\dfrac{10}{35} = \dfrac{2}{p}$

9. $\dfrac{2.5}{y} = \dfrac{5}{12}$

In Exercises 10–15, write the sentence as a proportion. Then solve.

10. x is to 5 as 12 is to 15

11. y is to 12 as 2 is to 3

12. 4 is to 9 as 24 is to z

13. 7 is to 11 as y is to 99

14. 3 is to 4 as w is to 18

15. t is to 10 as 3 is to 35

In Exercises 16–18, use a calculator to solve the proportion. Round your result to 2 decimal places.

16. $\dfrac{13}{15} = \dfrac{x}{35}$

17. $\dfrac{k}{6} = \dfrac{8}{15}$

18. $\dfrac{25}{32} = \dfrac{m}{18}$

In Exercises 19 and 20, find the lengths of the missing sides of the similar triangles.

19.

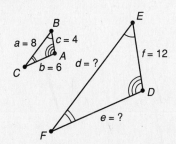

20.

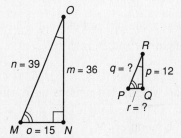

21. The recommended application for a particular type of lawn fertilizer is one 50-pound bag for 575 square feet. How many bags of this type of fertilizer would be required to fertilize 2875 square feet of lawn?

22. One hundred cement blocks are needed to build a wall 16-feet high. How many cement blocks are needed to build a wall 48-feet high?

23. A quality control engineer for a certain buyer found 2 defective parts in a sample of 50. At this rate, what is the expected number of defective parts in a shipment of 50,000.

1. Curtis School has 1575 students. The student to teacher ratio is 15 to 1. How many teachers are at Curtis School?

2. The speed of 50 miles per hour is equivalent to approximately 80 kilometers per hour.
   a. If you are traveling 35 mph, approximately how fast are you traveling in kilometers per hour?

   b. If you are traveling 110 kph and the speed limit is 65 mph, are you speeding? Explain.

3. A recipe calls for $2\frac{1}{2}$ cups of flour to make 2 dozen cookies. How many cups of flour would be required to bake 15 dozen cookies for a cookie sale?

4. A meteorologist reports that the ratio of snowfall in January to total snowfall during the average winter is 2 to 5. If 34 inches have fallen in January of the current year, find the predicted total snowfall for the entire winter.

5. Because of slumping sales, a small company had to lay off some of its employees. The ratio of total employees to employees laid off is 5 to 1. Find the total number of employees if 22 employees are laid off.

6. A crew of loggers felled and cleared $\frac{1}{2}$ acre of lumber in 4 days. How long will it take the same crew to fell and clear $2\frac{3}{4}$ acres of lumber?

7. A person who weighs 200 pounds on Earth would weigh about 32 pounds on the moon. Find the weight of a person on Earth who would weigh 15 pounds on the moon.

8. A pump can fill a 750-gallon tank in 35 minutes. How long will it take to fill a 1000-gallon tank with this same pump?

9. In a public opinion poll, 624 people from a sample of 1100 indicated they would vote for a specific candidate. Assuming this poll to be a correct indicator of the electorate, how many votes can the candidate expect to receive from a population of 40,000?

8.4

Name _____

In exercises 1–10, solve the percent equation. Round your answer to 2 decimal places.

1. 16 is what percent of 500?
2. What is 27 percent of 320?
3. What is 46% of 86?
4. 234 is 36 percent of what number?
5. 27 is 125% of what number?
6. 456 is $33\frac{1}{3}$% of what number?
7. What is 365% of 430?
8. 2.52 is 18% of what number?
9. 92 is what percent of 86?
10. What is 36% of 125?

In Exercises 11–14, use mental math to solve the percent equation.

11. 20 is 20% of what number?
12. What is 75% of 400?
13. 6 is what percent of 60?
14. 300 is 200% of what number?

In Exercises 15 and 16, find and correct the error. Then solve.

15. Problem: 25 is what percent of 675?

    Percent equation $\dfrac{a}{675} = \dfrac{25}{100}$

16. Problem: What is 52% of 162?

    Percent equation $\dfrac{100}{162} = \dfrac{p}{52}$

In Exercises 17–19, solve the percent equation. Then sketch a geometric model that illustrates your solution.

17. $\dfrac{125}{500} = \dfrac{p}{100}$

18. $\dfrac{a}{25} = \dfrac{80}{100}$

19. $\dfrac{36}{b} = \dfrac{45}{100}$

20. The annual auto insurance premium for a policyholder is normally $739. However, after having an automobile accident, the policyholder was charged an additional 32%. What is the new annual premium?

21. Suppose you buy a motorbike that costs $1450 plus 6% sales tax. Find the amount of sales tax, and the total bill.

22. A customer left $20 for a meal that cost $16.95. How much was the tip? What percent of the cost of the meal is the amount of the tip?

23. The monthly salary of an employee is $1000 plus a 7% commission on her total sales. How much must the employee sell in order to obtain a monthly salary of $3500?

In Exercises 1–4, use the following:

The circle graph shows a student's college expenses for an average school year. The student's tuition is $4250.

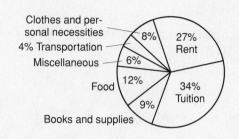

1. What is the total expenditure for the year?

2. How much is spent for rent?

3. How much is spent on books?

4. How much is spent on food?

In Exercises 5–11, use the table which shows the percent of the total land area of the Earth that each continent occupies. Write your answers in scientific notation. Round to 3 decimal places. The area of Europe is approximately 4.066×10^6 square miles.

5. What is the total land area of the Earth?

6. What is the land area of Africa?

7. What is the land area of Antarctica?

8. What is the land area of Asia?

9. What is the land area of Australia?

10. What is the land area of North America?

11. What is the land area of South America?

Continent	Percent of total land area
Africa	20.4%
Antarctica	8.9%
Asia	30.0%
Australia	5.2%
Europe	7.1%
North America	16.3%
South America	8.9%

12. World population reached 5.48×10^9 in mid-1992 according to the United Nations' estimates. According to the U.S. Bureau of Census, 75 out of every 100 people in the world today live in 22 countries. The other 25 live in the remaining 184 countries. The following are the six countries with the highest populations. Of every 100 people in the world, 21 live in China, 16 live in India, 5 live in the former Soviet Union, 5 live in the United States, 4 live in Indonesia, and 3 live in Brazil. Construct a table showing the percent of the world's population and the number of people living in each of these 6 countries. Write your answers in scientific notation. Round to 3 decimal places.

13. A advertisement states that a car on sale has been marked down $3167.50. It also states that this was a 15% discount. What was the original list price?

14. A girls softball team finished their regular season with only 2 losses. The newspaper reports that they won 95% of their games. How many games did they play? How many did they win?

15. A compact disc car stereo was purchased and a 5% sales tax was added. The stereo was $346.29. What was the amount of the sales tax?

In Exercises 1–6, decide whether the change is an increase or decrease
and find the percent.

1. Before: 12 After: 15

2. Before: 6 After: 4

3. Before: 125 After: 100

4. Before: 150 After: 175

5. Before: 200 After: 150

6. Before: 320 After: 336

In Exercises 7–10, decide whether the change is an increase or a decrease
and find the percent. Round to 1 decimal place.

7. November: $1.18
   December: $1.20

8. Opening day: $18.20
   Closing day: $16.80

9. Monday: $324.00
   Friday: $365.00

10. Beginning balance: $5002.00
    Ending balance: $4890.00

In Exercises 11–14, use percents to describe the pattern. Then list the next
three terms.

11. 2, 8, 32, 128, ? , ? , ?

12. 640, 320, 160, 80, ? , ? , ?

13. 1, 10, 100, 1000, ? , ? , ?

14. 15625, 6250, 2500, 1000, ? , ? , ?

In Exercises 15–18, decide whether the statement is true or false. Explain
your reasoning.

15. Three times a number is a 300% increase of
    the number.

16. One third a number is a $66\frac{2}{3}$% decrease of the
    number.

17. A 90% decrease of 60 is 54.

18. A 20% increase of 80 is 96.

In Exercises 19 and 20, describe a real-life situation that involves the given
decrease or increase.

19. A 100% increase

20. A decrease of 15%

21. Copy and complete the table.

22. In 1988, the number of tropical storms and hurricanes
    reaching the United States coastline was 12. In 1989,
    the number was 4. Find the percent decrease from
    1988 to 1989. (Source: Universal Almanac)

23. In 1970, the life expectancy at birth for a person
    born in the United States was 71 years. In 1991, it
    increased to 76. Find the percent increase from 1970
    to 1991. (Source: Universal Almanac)

Original Number	New Number	Percent Change
55	?	20% increase
55	?	20% decrease
?	350	75% increase
?	350	75% decrease
60	75	?
60	45	?

1. On a particular night at a restaurant, there is a special in which you can choose a dinner consisting of a cup of soup, one entree, one dessert, and a beverage, all for only $4.95. There are 4 kinds of soup, 10 entrees, 6 desserts and 3 different beverages. Use the counting principle to find how many different meals you could choose.

2. You need to buy a shirt and tie for a special occasion. There are five different colors of shirts and three different types of ties to choose from. Use the counting principle to find how many different combinations of a shirt and tie are possible. Then confirm your answer by listing the different combinations.

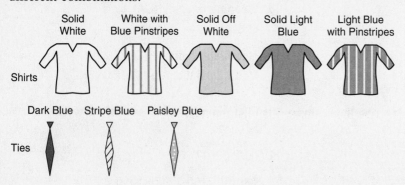

Shirts: Solid White   White with Blue Pinstripes   Solid Off White   Solid Light Blue   Light Blue with Pinstripes

Ties: Dark Blue   Stripe Blue   Paisley Blue

3. The members of the runner's club, Angel, Bo, Curtis, and Dave, are to have their picture taken for their yearbook. Use a tree diagram to find the number of different ways the four can stand in a row. If the four stand in random order, what is the probability that Angel and Bo will be standing next to each other?

4. The lock on your locker at school is a combination lock with 50 numbers on the dial. Three numbers are needed to unlock the lock and numbers can be repeated. How many different three number patterns are possible? What is the probability that you unlock the lock, not knowing the combination, the first time you try?

5. Television and radio stations are known by their call letters, for example, WQYX. The Federal Communications Commission (FCC) sets regulations for these broadcast stations. One regulation is that these call letters must be of a certain form. The first letter must be either a W or a K. The remaining three letters may be any letter of the alphabet and letters may be repeated. Use the counting principle to determine the total number of four letter combinations that are possible. If you choose one of the combinations at random, what is the probability that the one you choose has a second letter that is a Q?

6. You and a group of friends love to go to the movies. You always purchase popcorn, a soda, and candy. You can choose buttered or unbuttered popcorn, 5 different kinds of soda, and 18 different types of candy. How many different times can you go to the movies and not have the same snacks as you did the last time?

Name _____

In Exercises 1–4, two six-sided dice are rolled.

1. How many outcomes are possible?

2. List the outcomes that are possible using a tree diagram.

3. If the numbers that are rolled are added together, what is the smallest sum and the largest sum possible?

4. Find the probability of rolling the following sums:

   a. 2   **b.** 6, 9, or 10   **c.** 7

   d. An even number   **e.** At most 11   **f.** At least 7

5. Roll two six-sided dice 50 times and record the results. Find the experimental probabilities for each of the outcomes in Exercise 4. Compare the results to the theoretical probabilities. Write a short paragraph explaining your results.

In Exercises 6–8, a six question true-false exam was given.

6. How many ways could the exam be answered?

7. If you guessed on each question, what is the probability that you have a perfect score?

8. If you answered the first and third question correctly and guessed on the remaining questions, what is the probability that you have a perfect score?

In Exercises 9–11, you are on a game show. You have the chance to win a car. All that you have to do is to guess correctly the actual price of the car. The price is a five digit number. The diagram gives the choices for each digit.

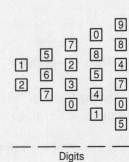

9. How many possible prices of the car exist?

10. What is the probability of choosing the correct price on your initial guess?

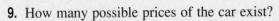

Digits

11. If you know the first two digits, what is the probability of winning?

In Exercises 1–6, write both square roots of the numbers.

1. 36   2. 12   3. 1.96

4. 0.64   5. 400   6. $\frac{25}{36}$

In Exercises 7–9, sketch the largest possible square that can be formed with the tiles. Use the result to determine which two whole numbers the square root of the number of original tiles is between.

7. 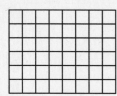   8. 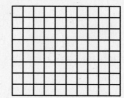   9.

In Exercises 10–15, write both solutions of the equation. Round each solution to three decimal places, if necessary.

10. $y^2 = 25$ 11. $q^2 = 625$ 12. $m^2 = 30$

13. $p^2 + 11 = 38$ 14. $5w^2 = 320$ 15. $9k^2 = 144$

In Exercises 16–18, the small squares on the grid are each 1 square unit. Estimate the side lengths of the shaded square. Use a calculator to confirm your estimate.

16.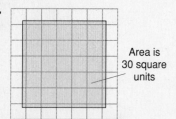

Area is 30 square units

17.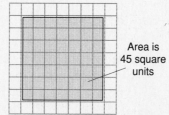

Area is 45 square units

18.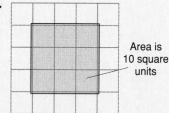

Area is 10 square units

In Exercises 19–21, write an algebraic equation for the sentence. Then solve the equation.

19. The square root of 121 is x.

20. The difference of q squared and 10 is 39.

21. The product of 25 and y squared is 49.

In Exercises 22–25, use the figure at the right and the following information. The perimeter of the square bedroom is 48 feet.

22. What are the dimensions of the bedroom?

23. When carpeting is laid in the bedroom and bath, 170 square feet is used. What is the area of the bathroom?

24. What are the approximate dimensions of the bathroom?

25. What is the approximate perimeter of the bathroom?

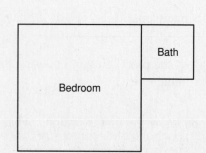

Bath

Bedroom

In Exercises 1–6, determine whether the number is rational or irrational. Explain your reasoning.

1. $\frac{13}{2}$

2. $-\frac{41}{19}$

3. $\sqrt{12}$

4. $-\sqrt{16}$

5. $-\sqrt{8}$

6. $\sqrt{\frac{9}{4}}$

In Exercises 7–10, complete the statement using **always**, **sometimes**, or **never**. Explain your reasoning.

7. A rational number is $\boxed{?}$ an integer.

8. A square root of a number is $\boxed{?}$ an irrational number.

9. An integer is $\boxed{?}$ a irrational number.

10. A rational number is $\boxed{?}$ a real number.

In Exercises 11–13, evaluate the expression for $a = 2$, $b = 9$ and $c = 36$. Is the result rational? Explain.

11. $\sqrt{a} \cdot \sqrt{b}$

12. $\sqrt{b} - \sqrt{c}$

13. $\sqrt{a} \div \sqrt{c}$

In Exercises 14–18, match the number with its graph.

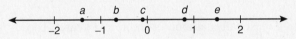

14. $-\sqrt{0.01}$

15. $-\sqrt{\frac{4}{9}}$

16. $-\sqrt{1.96}$

17. $\sqrt{2.25}$

18. $\frac{\sqrt{16}}{5}$

In Exercises 19–23, plot the number on the same number line.

19. $\frac{9}{2}$

20. $\sqrt{12}$

21. $-\sqrt{16}$

22. $\frac{\sqrt{5}}{2}$

23. $-\frac{\sqrt{16}}{3}$

In Exercises 24–29, complete the statement with $<$, $>$, or $=$.

24. $\sqrt{2} \ \square \ \frac{7}{5}$

25. $-\sqrt{\frac{9}{25}} \ \square \ -\frac{14}{25}$

26. $\frac{9.6}{0.6} \ \square \ \sqrt{2.56}$

27. $\sqrt{\frac{25}{36}} \ \square \ \sqrt{\frac{64}{81}}$

28. $-\sqrt{10} \ \square \ -\frac{81}{25}$

29. $\frac{\sqrt{625}}{9} \ \square \ \frac{14}{5}$

In Exercises 30–32, find the side lengths of the shaded squares. Leave your answer written with the square root symbol.

30.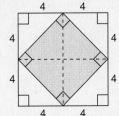

31.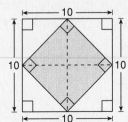

32.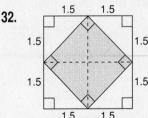

Name _____

In Exercises 1–9, a and b are the lengths of the legs of a right triangle, and c is the length of the hypotenuse. Find the missing length.

1. $a = 6, b = 8$ 2. $a = 15, c = 39$ 3. $b = 30, c = 50$

4. $a = 9, c = 41$ 5. $b = 24, c = 25$ 6. $a = 28, b = 45$

7. $a = 21, b = 28$ 8. $a = 40, c = 50$ 9. $b = 24, c = 30$

In Exercises 10–17, if possible, draw a right triangle whose sides have the given lengths.

10. 12, 35, 37   11. 10, 25, 26   12. 12, 16, 20   13. 15, 20, 25

14. 9, 13, 15   15. 3, 4, 5   16. 14, 49, 50   17. 27, 36, 45

In Exercises 18–20, find the length of the third side.

18.
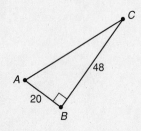

19.
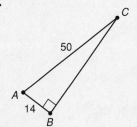

20.
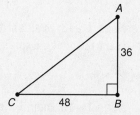

21. The instruction booklet for a 40 foot ladder states: When leaning against a vertical wall, the base of the ladder should be between 10 and 18 feet from the wall. Under those conditions, what are the maximum and minimum heights that the ladder will reach on the wall?

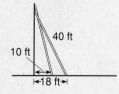

22. A baseball diamond is a perfect square. The distance between the bases is 90 feet. A base runner is on first and attempts to steal second. If the catcher is 3 feet behind home plate, how far must he throw the ball to reach second base?

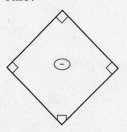

23. Due to road construction, a stretch of highway has to be closed. The detour runs 11 miles west and 13 miles south as shown. About how many miles of highway are closed?

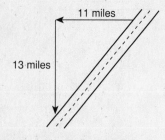

24. A radio station broadcast tower is anchored by four wires each 160 feet from the base of the tower. Each of those wires is 240 feet long. Find the height of the tower.

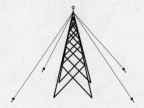

In Exercises 1–3, find the perimeter and area of the figure.

1.
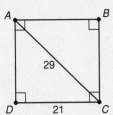

2.
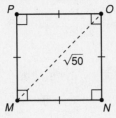

3.
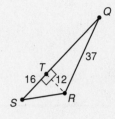

4. You are mounting an 8 foot TV antenna on your flat garage roof. The installation kit provides three cables each 10 feet in length that attach to the top of the antenna. How far should each of these cables be placed from the base of the antenna so that the antenna remains vertical?

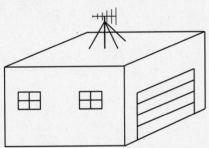

5. A plane flies in a straight line to Jacksonville. It is 100 miles east and 150 miles north of the point of departure, Osceola. How far did the plane fly?

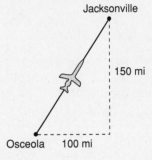

6. In a football game, a quarterback throws a pass from the 15-yard line, 10 yards from the sideline. The pass is caught on the 40-yard line, 45 yards from the same sideline. How long was the pass?

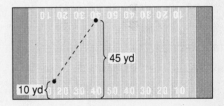

7. On a softball diamond, the bases are 60 feet apart and meet to form right angles. A base runner is standing on first when the batter hits a long fly ball down the right field line. The base runner takes off for second, rounds second, sprints for third, and slides headfirst into third. What a slide! However, it was a foul ball. So the runner gets up, and jogs straight across the infield back to first. How far did the runner run on this play?

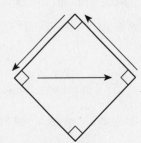

Name _____

In Exercises 1–6, graph the inequality.

1. $x \leq 3$ **2.** $x < 0$ **3.** $x \geq -10$

4. $x < -3$ **5.** $x > 9$ **6.** $x \geq 4$

In Exercises 7–12, write the inequality represented by the graph.

7.   **8.**

9.   **10.**

11.   **12.**

In Exercises 13–16, write the inequality given by the verbal phrase. Then graph the inequality.

13. All real numbers less than $\sqrt{10}$.   **14.** All real numbers greater than $\sqrt{11}$.

15. All real numbers greater than or equal to $-\sqrt{5}$.   **16.** All real numbers less than or equal to $-\sqrt{15}$.

In Exercises 17–22, solve the inequality. Then graph the solution.

17. $w + 4 \geq 3$ **18.** $x - 4 < -2$ **19.** $y + 5 < 2$

20. $r - 10 \leq 4$ **21.** $-2 < t + 6$ **22.** $16 < x + 9$

In Exercises 23–25, write an equivalent inequality. Then write the inequality verbally.

23. $x \geq 5$ **24.** $t \leq -10$ **25.** $w > -4$

In Exercises 26–29, write an algebraic model for the verbal phrase. Then solve.

26. q plus 12 is less than -4.   **27.** z minus 10 is less than or equal to 5.

28. The difference of p and 16 is greater than -12.   **29.** 42 is greater than or equal to the sum of t and 22.

In Exercises 30–33, write an algebraic model for the verbal model.

30. Vicki is at least 13 years old. Let a represent Vicki's age.   **31.** Mo hit more than 18 home runs this season. Let h represent the number of homers.

32. The temperatures never rose about $-5°$F yesterday. Let t represent the temperature.   **33.** You should study more than 2 hours per day. Let h represent the number of hours.

In Exercises 34 and 35, write a real life situation that can be represented by the graph.

34.   **35.**

In Exercises 1 and 2, describe the error. Then solve the inequality correctly.

1.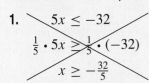

2.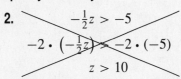

In Exercises 3–6, match the solution of the inequality to its graph.

a. ◄——+——+——●——+——+——►
   -6 -5 -4 -3 -2

b. ◄——+——+——+——⊕——+——►
   -5 -4 -3 -2 -1

c. ◄——+——⊕——+——+——+——►
   11 12 13 14 15

d. ◄——+——+——●——+——+——►
   -8 -7 -6 -5 -4

3. $-\frac{1}{3}z < -4$

4. $6x < -12$

5. $\frac{1}{4} \geq -\frac{1}{16}z$

6. $0.3w \leq -1.8$

In Exercises 7–18, solve the inequality. Then graph its solution.

7. $5n < 12$

8. $-3m < 11$

9. $\frac{x}{4} \geq 6$

10. $25 \geq 15k$

11. $\frac{3}{8} < -4c$

12. $-\frac{3}{4} \leq \frac{5}{4}w$

13. $-\frac{2}{5}p \leq 10$

14. $19 \geq -6m$

15. $15 < 0.4p$

16. $\frac{a}{12} < -6$

17. $14d < -21$

18. $-3.2w < 1.28$

19. You are recycling aluminum cans to save enough money to buy a new portable CD player which costs $120.75. The recycling center is paying 35¢ per pound of aluminum. How many pounds of aluminum cans do you need to recycle to have at least $120.75?

20. You and your family are traveling to the mountains for a weekend vacation. The last sign you saw said that your destination is still 255 miles away. Your parents say that you'll be there in at most $4\frac{1}{2}$ hours. How fast will your family have to travel to arrive in at most $4\frac{1}{2}$ hours?

21. Your family has added a new room to your home. You've budgeted $450 for carpeting. The room has a floor area of 30 square yards. What is the most you can spend per square yard so that the cost of the carpeting is not more than $450?

22. You're taping some of your favorite singles onto a 90 minute blank cassette. On average each of your favorite singles is 4 minutes 30 seconds. What is the greatest number of singles that can be recorded without cutting any song short?

Name _____

In Exercises 1 and 2, describe the error. Then correct it.

1. $-3x - 2 \le 5$

$-3x - 2 + 2 \le 5 + 2$

$\dfrac{-3x}{-3} \le \dfrac{7}{-3}$

$x \le -\dfrac{7}{3}$

2. $5(3y + 2) > -3$

$15y + 10 > -3$

$15y + 10 - 10 < -3 - 10$

$15y < -13$

$y < -\dfrac{13}{15}$

In Exercises 3 and 4, decide whether the statement is sometimes, always, or never true.

3. If $5(4 - 2x) < 10$, then $x < 1$.

4. If $2(-3x + 4) > 12 - 16x$, then $x > \frac{2}{5}$.

In Exercises 5–8, match the inequality with its solution.

a. $x < 5$ **b.** $x < -5$ **c.** $x > -5$ **d.** $x > 5$

5. $3(x + 3) < -6$

6. $2(10x - 1) < 4x + 6(x + 8)$

7. $3x + 1 > -7(x + 7)$

8. $\frac{4}{5}x > 3\left(\frac{1}{5}x - 1\right) + 4$

In Exercises 9–14, solve the inequality.

9. $7x + 2 < -19$

10. $\frac{1}{9}z + 11 \ge -9$

11. $2a + 7 < -5a + 28$

12. $\frac{3}{8}x \le \frac{1}{8}x + 10$

13. $8(x - 3) \ge 2x + 6$

14. $-3x + 19 > -5x$

In Exercises 15–17, let $2n$, $2n + 2$, **and** $2n + 4$ **be three consecutive even integers. Write the inequality that represents the verbal sentence. Then solve the inequality.**

15. The sum of three consecutive even integers is less than or equal to 18.

16. The sum of three consecutive even integers is more than 66.

17. The sum of three consecutive even integers is less than -12.

In Exercises 18 and 19, find the possible values of x.

18. The perimeter of the rectangle is at most 36 square centimeters.

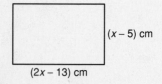

$(x - 5)$ cm

$(2x - 13)$ cm

19. The area of the triangle is more than 40 square feet.

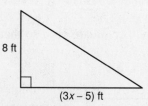

8 ft

$(3x - 5)$ ft

20. Suppose you are taking a senior level calculus class in which the grade is based on six 100-point exams. To earn an A in the course, you must have a total of at least 90% of the points. Your scores on the first five exams are 85, 92, 88, 96, and 87, respectively. How many points do you have to obtain on the sixth exam to earn an A in the course?

Name _____

In Exercises 1–4, can the side lengths be correct? Explain.

1.

2.

3.

4.

5. Copy and complete the table.

Measure of side 1	Measure of side 2	Measure of side 3 is greater than	Measure of side 3 is less than
4 in.	10 in.		
9 cm	17 cm		
12 ft	20 ft		
45 m	75 m		
125 yd	170 yd		

In Exercises 6–11, can the numbers be side lengths of a triangle?

6. $\frac{3}{8}, \frac{5}{8}, \frac{7}{8}$

7. $\sqrt{2}, \sqrt{5}, \sqrt{10}$

8. 3.24, 6.98, 10.18

9. $\sqrt{22}, 5, \sqrt{90}$

10. $\frac{1}{3}, \frac{1}{6}, \frac{1}{9}$

11. 10.29, 12.89, 23.18

In Exercises 12–15, use the figure at the right to complete the statement.

12. $a + c > \boxed{?}$

13. $a + \boxed{?} > e$

14. $e + d + c > \boxed{?}$

15. $b + c > \boxed{?}$

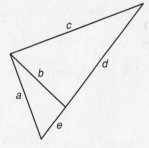

16. You are given a 14-inch piece of rope. Your instructions are to cut the rope and form a triangle. The only restriction is that you can only cut the rope into lengths that are integers. List the side lengths of all the possible triangles that could be formed.

17. Is it possible to form a triangle with side lengths of
  a. three consecutive integers?
  b. three consecutive even integers?
  c. three consecutive odd integers?
  Explain your results.

18. You have purchased a triangular piece of land and are planning to build a fence along the entire perimeter. You already have measurements from two sides which are 310 feet and 275 feet. What are the possible lengths for the third side? How much fencing must you purchase to ensure that you have enough fencing to enclose the entire area? How much fencing could you possibly have remaining after you complete the job?

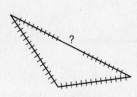

In Exercises 1–6, use the diagram at the right.

1. Name 3 different line segments that lie on $\overleftrightarrow{OU}$.

2. Name 5 rays that have beginning point P.

3. Name 2 pairs of lines that intersect.

4. Name 2 lines that appear parallel.

5. Name a ray in the opposite direction of $\overrightarrow{PO}$.

6. What is another name for the line segment $\overline{PR}$?

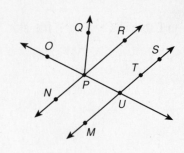

In Exercises 7–10, to use the diagram at the right decide whether the given symbol is a line, a line segment, a ray, or the length of a line segment.

7. $\overrightarrow{BE}$ 8. $\overleftrightarrow{BC}$ 9. BD 10. $\overline{AB}$

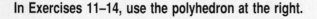

In Exercises 11–14, use the polyhedron at the right.

11. How many planes form the polyhedron's faces?

12. Name 5 points that lie in the same plane.

13. Name 3 lines that appear parallel to $\overleftrightarrow{AB}$.

14. Name 3 rays that have the beginning point I.

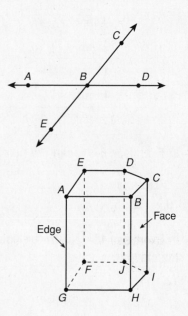

In Exercises 15 and 16, draw the indicated figure.

15. 3 lines, 2 of which do not intersect

16. 4 lines that intersect in one point

In Exercises 17–19, use the drawing of the lion cage.

17. Does the ceiling of the cage appear to be parallel to the floor of the cage?

18. On each side, do the vertical steel bars appear parallel?

19. What would you consider each side of the cage to be, in terms of the words of geometry?

In Exercises 1–4, use the figure at the right.

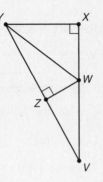

1. List the acute angles.

2. List the obtuse angles.

3. List the right angles.

4. List all angles with vertex W.

In Exercises 5–8, without using a protractor, match the angle with its measure.

a. $80°$ b. $175°$ c. $26°$ d. $120°$

5.
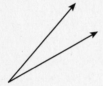

6.

7.
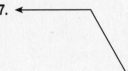

8.

In Exercises 9 and 10, use a protractor to draw the angle.

9. $35°$

10. $95°$

In Exercises 11 and 12, use a protractor to measure the angle.

In Exercises 13 and 14, measure and name the angles formed by the clock hands.

11.
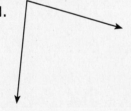

12.
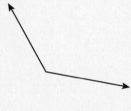

13.

14.
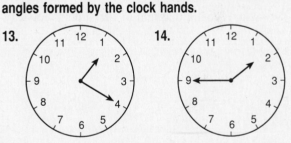

In Exercises 15–17, match the pairs of congruent angles.

a.

b.
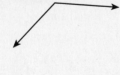

c.
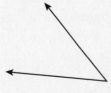

15.
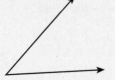

16.
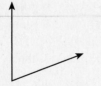

17.

10.3

Name _____

In Exercises 1–5, use the figure at the right.

1. Which two lines are parallel?

2. Is ∠12 congruent to ∠8? Why or why not?

3. List all angles whose measure is 55°.

4. List all angles whose measure is 85°.

5. Name two corresponding angles that have the same measure.

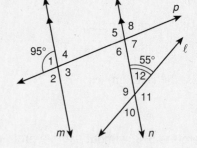

6. Explain why the indicated angles are congruent.

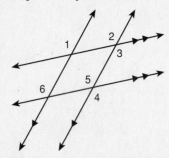

In Exercises 7–9, use the diagram of the city streets and the information. The north side of Morgan Road and the east side of Ryan Street meet to form a 75° angle. The west side of Danver Drive and the north side of Morgan Road meet to form a 105° angle.

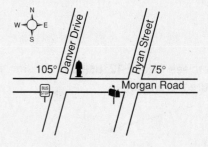

7. Draw and label a diagram of the streets. Identify the location of mailbox, bus stop and fire hydrant.

8. Present a case to explain why Danver Drive and Ryan Street are parallel.

9. Find measures of the angles (or intersection) at which the mailbox, bus stop, and fire hydrant are placed.

10. Chef Carlo Vincento wishes to decorate his world famous strawberry pie with fresh strawberries. He wishes to place these strawberries at the intersections of the parallel lines of whipped cream. However, for cosmetic appearances, the strawberries are only to be placed at congruent angles to the initial strawberry. Place a dot at every congruent angle to the one marked on the figure.

10.4

Name _____

In Exercises 1–3, identify any symmetry of the figure.

1.

2.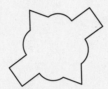

3.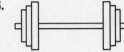

In Exercises 5–8, identify any rotational symmetry in the figures.

4.

5.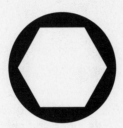

6.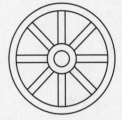

In Exercises 7 and 8, copy the grid of squares on a piece of paper. Then shade the unit squares so that the resulting figure has the indicated symmetry.

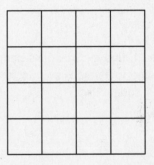

7. A vertical line of symmetry, but no horizontal line of symmetry and no rotational symmetry.

8. A rotational symmetry of $90°$, but no line of symmetry.

9. Plot the point $A(2, 4)$ in a coordinate plane. Locate points B, C, D so that $ABCD$ is a rectangle that has:

   a. a horizontal line of symmetry at the x-axis and no vertical line of symmetry at the y-axis

   b. a vertical line of symmetry at the y-axis and no horizontal line of symmetry at the x-axis

10. Plot the point $A(0, -5)$ in a coordinate plane. Locate points B and C so that ABC is a triangle that has:

   a. a line of symmetry at the x-axis only

   b. a line of symmetry at the y-axis only

10.5

Name _____

In Exercises 1–3, sketch the indicated type of triangle. Then label it with appropriate side or angle marks.

1. Right scalene

2. Obtuse scalene

3. Acute isosceles

In Exercises 4–6, classify the triangle according to its sides and angles.

4.

5.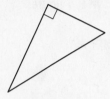

6.

In Exercises 7 and 8, use a protractor to draw $\triangle ABC$ with the given angle measures. Then classify the triangle according to its sides and angles.

7. $m\angle A = 45°$,
$m\angle B = 90°$,
$m\angle C = 45°$

8. $m\angle A = 35°$,
$m\angle B = 65°$,
$m\angle C = 80°$

In Exercises 9–11, find the triangle's perimeter and area. Then classify the triangle according to its sides and angles. (The area of each small square on the grid is 1 square unit.)

9.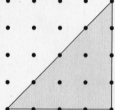

10.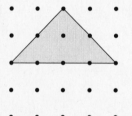

11.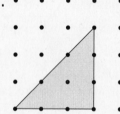

In Exercises 12–14, classify the triangle by its sides and by its angles.

12.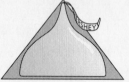

13.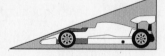

14.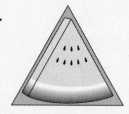

In Exercises 15–18, complete the statements using the words always, sometimes or never.

15. An isosceles triangle is ⬚ ? a right triangle.

16. An obtuse triangle is ⬚ ? a right triangle.

17. A right triangle is ⬚ ? an equilateral triangle.

18. A right triangle is ⬚ ? an isosceles triangle.

10.6

In Exercises 1–3, identify the quadrilateral from its appearance. Use the name that best describes the quadrilateral.

1.

2.

3.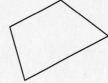

In Exercises 4 and 5, complete the statement with always, **sometimes**, or **never**. Explain your reasoning.

4. A rectangle is ? a square.

5. A parallelogram is ? a trapezoid.

In Exercises 6 and 7, find the values of x and y.

6. Rectangle

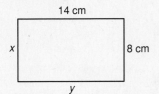

14 cm

x 8 cm

y

7. Rhombus

16 yd

x

y

In Exercises 8 and 9, use the description to sketch the figure. If it is not possible, write not possible.

8. A parallelogram with only 1 pair of congruent sides

9. A quadrilateral with two pair of parallel sides

In Exercises 10–12, use your conjecture from Exercise 35 on page 465 of the textbook to find $m\angle A$. Then name the quadrilateral.

10.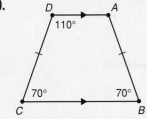

11.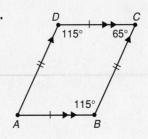

12.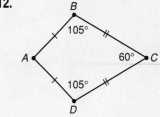

In Exercises 1–3, match the quadrilateral with a congruent quadrilateral.

a.

b.

c.

1.

2.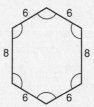

3.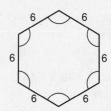

4. Which of the following polygons are equilateral? Which are equiangular? Which are regular?

a.

b.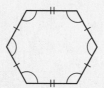

c.

In Exercises 5–7 , use the words equilateral, equiangular, and regular to describe the polygon.

5.

6.

7.

In Exercises 8–10, draw the figure and mark any congruent sides or angles.

8. A regular pentagon

9. A convex hexagon

10. A non-convex quadrilateral

In Exercises 11–13, solve for x and find the length of each side.

11. The perimeter is 50.

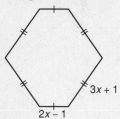

2x − 1 · 3x + 1

12. The perimeter is 69.

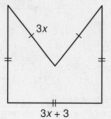

3x · 3x + 3

13. The perimeter is 104.

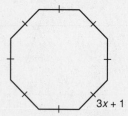

3x + 1

10.8

Name _____

In Exercises 1–3, find the measure of ∠x.

1.

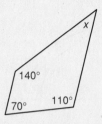

2.

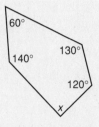

3.

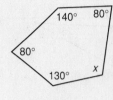

In Exercises 4–6, you are given the measure of each interior angle of a regular polygon. How many sides does the polygon have?

4. $108°$

5. $140°$

6. $150°$

In Exercises 7–9, you are given the measure of each exterior angle of a regular polygon. How many sides does the polygon have?

7. $40°$

8. $60°$

9. $120°$

In Exercises 10–12, you are given the number of sides of a regular polygon. Find the measure of each interior and exterior angle.

10. 10

11. 6

12. 18

In Exercises 13 and 14, you are shown part of a convex n-gon. The pattern of congruent angles continues around the polygon. Find n. (Hint: If the sum of the exterior angles is $360°$, how many sides are there?)

13.

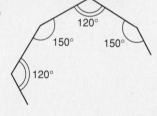

14.

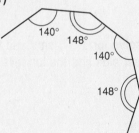

In Exercises 15 and 16, find the measure of each angle.

15.

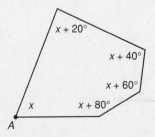

Angle increases $20°$ clockwise

16.

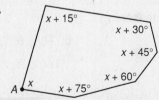

Angle increases $15°$ clockwise

10.9

Name _____

In Exercises 1–3, state the shortest and longest sides of the triangle.

1.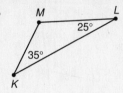

2.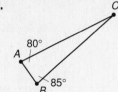

3.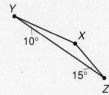

In Exercises 4–6, state the smallest and largest angles of the triangle.

4.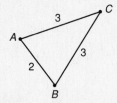

5.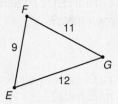

6.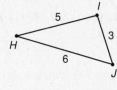

In Exercises 7 and 8, order the sides from shortest to longest.

7.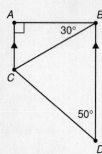

8.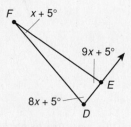

In Exercises 9 and 10, solve for x. Then name the smallest angle, the largest angle, the shortest side and the longest side of the triangle.

9.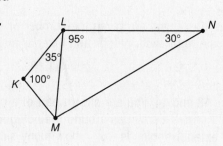

10. F $x + 5°$
   $9x + 5°$
   E
   $8x + 5°$ D

In Exercises 11–13, match the angle measures with the approximate side lengths. Explain your reasoning.

a. $40°, 50°, 90°$ **b.** $60°, 60°, 60°$ **c.** $30°, 75°, 75°$

11. 2, 2, 2   **12.** 5, 8, 8   **13.** 7, 9, 11.4

14. Buck Springs is 60 miles N30°E of Angel Falls. San José is 40 miles due east of Angel Falls. Buck Springs is also N10°W of San José. Use a protractor and straight edge to sketch a diagram of the three towns. Then determine which two towns are the furthest apart and which two are the nearest. The distance between Buck Springs and San José must be between what two values?

In Exercises 1 and 2, find the area of each figure. Describe two ways to find the area of the second figure.

1.
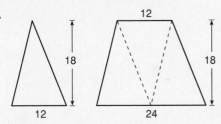

2.
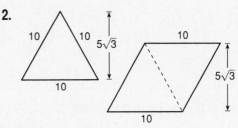

In Exercises 3 and 4, show how the first figure can be used to find the area of the second. Then find the perimeter of each figure.

3.
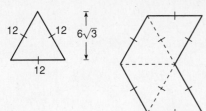

4.
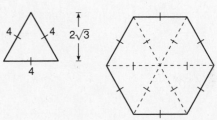

In Exercises 5 and 6, make a sketch on dot paper to represent the "equation." Then find the area and perimeter of the final figure.

5. (2 Congruent Right Triangles) + (2 Equilateral Triangles) = (1 Rectangle)

6. (2 Isosceles Trapezoids) + (2 Congruent Isosceles Triangles) = (1 Parallelogram)

7. The garage roof shown is made from two isosceles trapezoids and two isosceles triangles. Find the area of the entire roof.

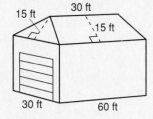

8. You are mowing your lawn, as shown. The mower cuts a path 18 inches wide. If you cut 48 paths parallel to the base, what is the area of the lawn which you have cut?

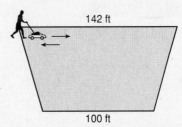

9. You are repairing a large replica of the HOLLYWOOD sign in California. The plans for the "D" are shown. Each square represents 1 square foot. Find the area of the letter.

In Exercises 1–6, use the fact that $\triangle ABC \cong \triangle XYZ$ to complete the statement.

1. $\angle A \cong$ ⬚   2. $\overline{BC} \cong$ ⬚

3. $\angle C \cong$ ⬚   4. ⬚ $\cong \overline{YZ}$

5. ⬚ $\cong \angle Y$ 6. ⬚ $\cong \overline{XZ}$

In Exercises 7–10, complete the statement.

7. If $\triangle ABC \cong \triangle DEF$, then $\overline{AC} \cong$ ⬚ .   8. If $\triangle ABC \cong \triangle MNO$, then $\angle B \cong$ ⬚ .

9. If $\triangle STU \cong \triangle XYZ$, then $m\angle S =$ ⬚ .   10. If $\triangle DEF \cong \triangle MNO$, then $EF =$ ⬚ .

11. List each pair of congruent polygons.

a.   b.   c.   d.

12. Two of the figures are congruent. Which are they?

a.   b.   c.   d.

In Exercises 13–15, divide the region into two congruent parts.

13.   14.   15.

In Exercises 16–18, divide the region into four congruent parts.

16.   17.   18.

In Exercises 19 and 20, use the square grid. Each small square has sides of one unit.

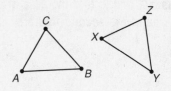

19. How many 1-unit congruent squares are in the grid?

20. How many 2-unit by 2-unit congruent squares are in the grid?

11.3

Name _____

In Exercises 1–5, consider the coordinates $X(-3, 4)$, $Y(-1, 2)$, and $Z(-4, 1)$ of $\triangle XYZ$. Find the coordinates of the image after the indicated reflection(s).

1. Reflect about the x-axis

2. Reflect about the y-axis

3. Reflect about the x-axis, then about the y-axis

4. Reflect about the y-axis, then about the x-axis

5. Reflect about the y-axis, then again about the y-axis

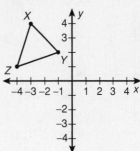

In Exercises 6–8, draw the reflection of the figure in line l.

6.

7.
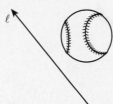

8.
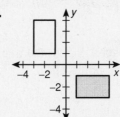

In Exercises 9–11, is the shaded figure a reflection of the unshaded figure in l?

9.
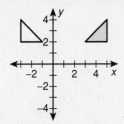

10.

11.

In Exercises 12–14, draw the line that can be used to reflect the unshaded figure to the shaded figure.

12.
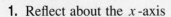

13.
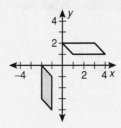

14.

15. Which letters of the alphabet look like the same letter when reflected about a vertical line? List them.

16. Use a mirror to decode the secret message.
    "TOH OOT HTOUM YM MOM HO"

17. Use the letters from Exercise 15 to write your own coded message.

11.4

Name _____

In Exercises 1–3, the unshaded figure is rotated clockwise about the origin to produce the shaded figure. Find the angle of rotation.

1.

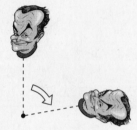

2.

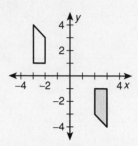

3.

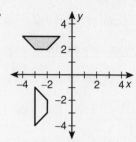

In Exercises 4–6, estimate the angle and direction of rotation.

4.

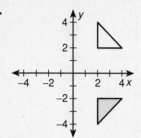

5.

6.

In Exercises 7–12, find the image of the segment or triangle.

7. 90° clockwise rotation of $\overline{BC}$ about O.

8. 90° clockwise rotation of $\overline{JD}$ about O.

9. 90° counterclockwise rotation of $\overline{QL}$ about O.

10. 90° counterclockwise rotation of $\overline{OM}$ about O.

11. 180° rotation of $\triangle DEF$ about O.

12. 180° rotation of $NJPO$ about O.

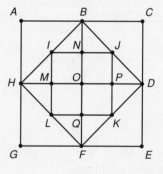

In Exercises 13–15, draw the figure on tracing paper. Rotate the tracing paper as indicated about point O. Then trace the figure again.

13. 90° counterclockwise

14. 180°

15. 60° clockwise

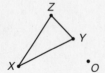

In Exercises 1–3, match the graph with the ordered pair that describes the translation. Then describe the translation verbally.

a.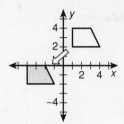

b.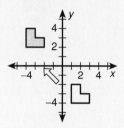

c.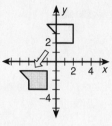

1. $(x - 5, y + 6)$ **2.** $(x - 3, y - 5)$ **3.** $(x - 5, y - 4)$

In Exercises 4–6, use the figure at the right to match the translation of $\square ABCD$ to $\square A'B'C'D'$ with the ordered pair that describes the translation.

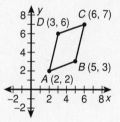

a. $A'(1, 4), B'(4, 5), C'(5, 9), D'(2, 8)$

b. $A'(2, 1), B'(5, 2), C'(6, 6), D'(3, 5)$

c. $A'(3, 2), B'(6, 3), C'(7, 7), D'(4, 6)$

4. $(x + 1, y)$ **5.** $(x - 1, y + 2)$ **6.** $(x, y - 1)$

In Exercises 7–9, use a straightedge and dot paper to translate the figure by the ordered pair.

7. $(x + 1, y + 1)$

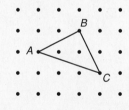

8. $(x - 1, y - 2)$

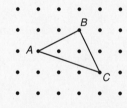

9. $(x, y - 1)$

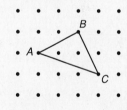

10. Find the name of Carl's dog. The dog's name has five letters. Given are the four ordered pairs that enable you to find the pup's name. Start at $(1, 1)$ on the grid and write down each letter you land on according to the transformation.

1. Start at $(1, 1)$
2. $(x + 3, y + 7)$
3. $(x - 2, y - 4)$
4. $(x + 5, y - 2)$
5. $(x + 2, y + 7)$

11. Write your own message by giving the ordered pair transformations and a starting point.

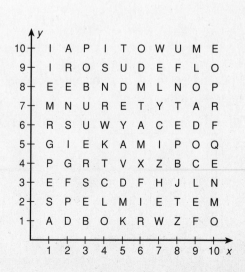

11.6

Name _____

1. Which two figures are similar?

a.  **b.**  **c.**   **d.**

In Exercises 2 and 3, you are given the length and width of three rectangles. Which two are similar?

2. a. 3 cm × 15 cm
   b. 3 ft × 15 in.
   c. 6 cm × 30 cm

3. a. $\frac{3}{2}$ cm × $\frac{7}{2}$ cm
   b. 21 in. × 49 in.
   c. 1 ft ×3 ft

In Exercises 4 and 5, determine whether the polygons are similar. If they are, find the scale factor of A to B.

4.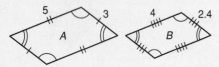

5.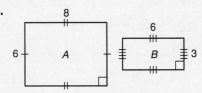

In Exercises 6–9, trapezoids $ABCD$ and $JKLM$ are similar, as shown at the right.

6. Write four equal ratios for $ABCD$ and $JKLM$.

7. Find the scale factor of $ABCD$ to $JKLM$.

8. Find the following:
   a. BC **b.** ML **c.** KJ

9. $m\angle C = m\angle$ $\boxed{?}$

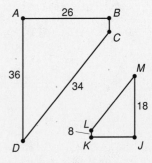

In Exercises 10–12, determine the scale factor (large to small) of the similar figures. Then solve for x.

10.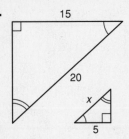

11.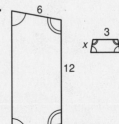

12.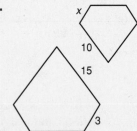

Name _____

1. You have purchased a scale model of a Jeep. The scale factor is 1 to 24. The model is 2.9 in. high, 2.75 in. wide, and 6.4 in. long. Find the dimensions, in feet, of the actual Jeep.

2. The map of the lake area below is drawn with a scale factor of 1 in. to 40 feet. Find the greatest distance across the lake.

In Exercises 3–5, use the diagram of the rectangular farm. The diagram is drawn with a scale factor of 1 cm to 44 m.

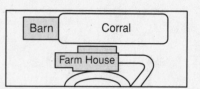

3. Find the perimeter of the entire farm.

4. Find the area of the entire farm.

5. If 1 acre $\approx 4047\,m^2$ yards, find the approximate number of acres the farm covers.

6. The distance from Pittsburgh to Philadelphia is about 250 miles. Use the map to approximate the distance from Erie to Philadelphia.

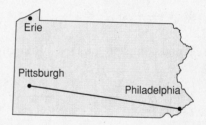

In Exercises 7–12, use the following information. The dimensions of a practice football field are $53\frac{1}{3}$ yards wide by 120 yards long.

7. What are the dimension of a model field with a scale factor of 40:1.

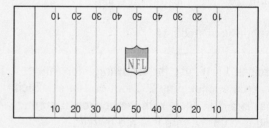

8. What is the perimeter of the practice field? Use the scale factor of 40:1 and Theorem 8.1 to find the perimeter of the model field.

9. How does the perimeter of the practice field compare to the perimeter of the scale model?

10. What would be the dimensions of a similar model field with scale factor of 1440:1? (Hint: Convert the dimensions to inches.)

11. Measure the figure. Is this figure similar to the practice field?

12. How tall would a player be if he is $\frac{1}{16}$ in. tall on the 1440:1 scale model field?

11.8

Name _____

In Exercises 1–6, use the triangle to find the trigonometric ratio.

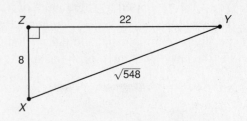

1. $\sin X$
2. $\sin Y$
3. $\cos X$
4. $\cos Y$
5. $\tan X$
6. $\tan Y$

In Exercises 7 and 8, solve the triangle for its unlabeled angle and side. Then write six trigonometric ratios that can be formed with the triangle.

7.

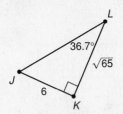

8.

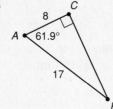

In Exercises 9 and 10, draw a right triangle, $\triangle MNO$, that has the given trigonometric ratios.

9. $\tan M = \dfrac{4}{\sqrt{27}}$, $\sin N = \dfrac{\sqrt{27}}{\sqrt{43}}$

10. $\cos N = \dfrac{7}{25}$, $\tan M = \dfrac{7}{24}$

11. Copy and complete the table. Round to 3 decimal places.

x	$80°$	$40°$	$20°$	$10°$	$5°$	$1°$
$\sin x$						
$\tan x$						

12. Compare the values of $\sin x$ and $\tan x$ as x gets smaller. Describe the relationship.

13. Explain your findings.

In Exercises 14–16, use the following information. A 100 foot tower is anchored by 200 foot guy wires. Each guy wire makes a $30°$ angle with the horizontal ground. Placed every 50 feet up the wire is a red marker.

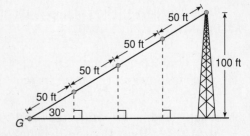

14. Find the vertical distance from each marker perpendicular to the ground.

15. Write the sine ratio for $\angle G$ for each triangle formed by the marker, the point directly beneath it, and the point, G, at which the guy wire is attached.

16. Explain your results.

11.9

Name _____

In Exercises 1–3, find the value of the trigonometric ratio. Round your answer to four decimal places.

1. $\tan 62°$

2. $\cos 57°$

3. $\sin 89°$

In Exercises 4–6, find the length of the labeled side. Round your results to two decimal places.

4.
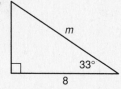

5.
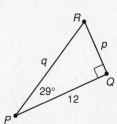

6.
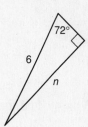

In Exercises 7–9, solve the right triangle for all labeled sides and angles. Round your results to two decimal places.

7.
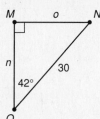

8.
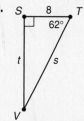

9.

10. From a 150 feet observation tower on the coast, a coast guard officer sights a boat in difficulty. The angle of depression of the boat is $4°$, as shown. How far is the boat from the shoreline?

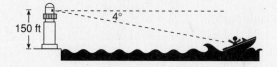

11. A train is traveling up a slight grade with an angle of inclination of only $2°$. After traveling 1 mile, what is the vertical change in feet? (1 mile = 5280 feet)

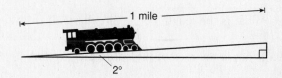

12. Use the diagram to find the distance across the bridge.

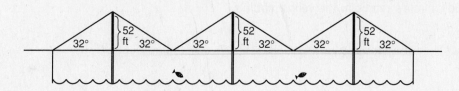

In Exercises 1–4, find the circumference and area of the figure. Use 3.14 for π. Round your result to one decimal place.

1.

$r = 6.1$ in.

2.

$d = 2.2$ in.

3.

$d = 2.8$ ft

4.

$r = 14.2$ in.

In Exercises 5 and 6, find the radius and diameter of the figure. Use 3.14 for π. Round your result to one decimal place.

In Exercises 7 and 8, find the area of the shaded portion of the figure. Use 3.14 for π. Round your result to one decimal place.

5.

$A = 735.0$ in.^{2}

6.

$C = 57.8$ cm

7.

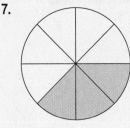

$r = 5$ cm

8.

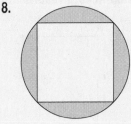

$d = 10$ in.

In Exercises 9 and 10, use the following information and the diagram. The shape of the outfield fence in a baseball stadium is that of a quarter circle. The distance from home plate to the wall is 330 feet. Use 3.14 for π.

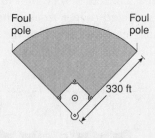

9. What is the length of the circular wall from foul pole to foul pole?

10. What is the area of the entire playing field?

In Exercises 11 and 12, use the following information and the diagram. The center yellow bull's eye has a radius of 2 inches. The ratio of the outer circle's radius to the middle circle's radius to the yellow circle's radius is 5 to 3 to 1. Use 3.14 for π.

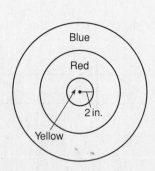

11. Find the radius of the middle circle and the outer circle.

12. Find the area of each colored area.

In Exercises 1–3, give the mathematical name of the solid.

1.
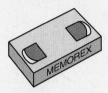

2.

3.

In Exercises 4–9, draw the solid that can be folded from the net.

4.
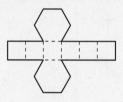

5.
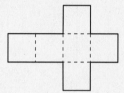

6.
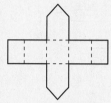

7.
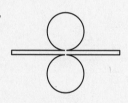

8.
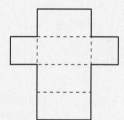

9.
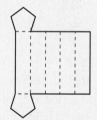

10. Use the figure shown which represents a barn.

   a. How many faces does the barn have?

   b. How many vertices does the barn have?

   c. How many edges does the barn have?

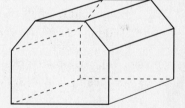

11. Use the figure shown which represents a piece of cake.

   a. How many faces does the piece of cake have?

   b. How many vertices does the piece of cake have?

   c. How many edges does the piece of cake have?

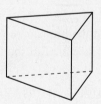

12. Use the shown figure which represents a 30-story luxury beach condominium.

   a. How many faces does the condominium have?

   b. How many vertices does the condominium have?

   c. How many edges does the condominium have?

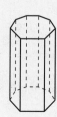

In Exercises 1–6, find the surface area of the right prism or right cylinder.
Use 3.14 for π. Round your results to one decimal place.

1.

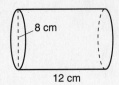

8 cm

12 cm

2.

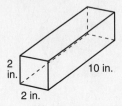

2 in.

2 in.

10 in.

3.

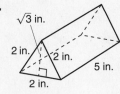

$\sqrt{3}$ in.

2 in.

2 in.

2 in.

5 in.

4.

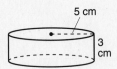

5 cm

3 cm

5.

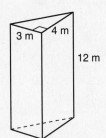

3 m

4 m

12 m

6.

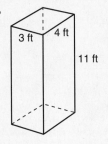

3 ft

4 ft

11 ft

7. Perform the following steps to find the surface area of the solid.
Use 3.14 for π. Round your results to one decimal place.

Step 1: Find the area of a base (the area of the larger circle minus the area of the smaller circle.)

Step 2: Find the area of the outside lateral surface (the diameter of the large circle times π times the height.)

Step 3: Find the area of the inside lateral surface (the diameter of the small circle times π times the height.)

Step 4: Add the areas. (Remember to add 2 bases.)

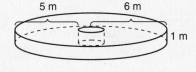

5 m   6 m   1 m

In Exercises 8–11, use the blocks at the right. Each block is 3
inches by 3 inches by 3 inches.

8. Find the surface area of one cube.

9. Imagine that the blocks are placed side by side to spell "APE".
Find the surface area of the new solid.

10. Is the result from Exercise 9 three times the result of Exercise
8? Explain.

11. Find the surface area if the blocks spell "PEA".

12. Find the surface area of a nickel. For best results find the
surface area in millimeters.

12.4

Name _____

In Exercises 1–4, find the volume of the solid.

1. A cube with 6 cm edges

2. A rectangular prism that is 5 in. by 6 in. by 3 in.

3. A right triangle prism with base area of 30 m^2 and height of 12 m.

4. A prism with hexagonal base area of 467.6 cm^2 and height of 10 cm.

In Exercises 5–7, solve for x.

5.
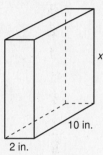
$V = 320$ in.^{3}

6.
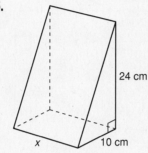
24 cm

$V = 2160$ cm^3

7.
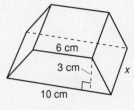
6 cm

3 cm

10 cm

x

$V = 240$ m^3

In Exercises 8–10, draw the prism formed by the net. Then find its volume.

8.
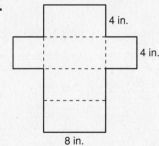
4 in.

4 in.

8 in.

9.
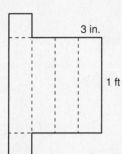
3 in.

1 ft

10.
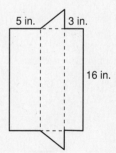
5 in. 3 in.

16 in.

11. How much plaster of paris is needed to make four miniature pillars for a model of a home if the pillars are square based prisms with a height of 12 in. and face width of 2 in.?

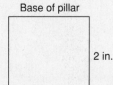
Base of pillar

2 in.

2 in.

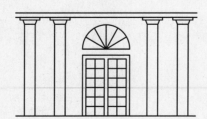

12.5

In Exercises 1–14, use 3.14 **for** π.

1. Find the volume of a cylinder with a radius of 2 meters and a height of 4 meters.

2. Find the volume of a cylinder with a base area of 625π in.^{2} and a height of 25 inches.

3. Find the volume of a cylinder with a diameter of 16 inches and a height of 4 inches.

4. Find the volume of a cylinder with a circumference of 25π and a height of 7.5 cm. (Hint: Use the circumference to find the radius.)

In Exercises 5–8, find the volume of the cylinder.

5.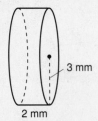

3 mm

2 mm

6.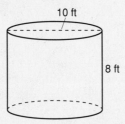

10 ft

8 ft

7.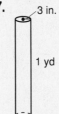

3 in.

1 yd

8.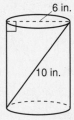

6 in.

10 in.

In Exercises 9–12, find the radius of the base or the height.

9.

4 in.

h

$v = 1105.08$ in.^{3}

10.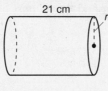

21 cm

r

$v = 3231.06$ cm^3

11.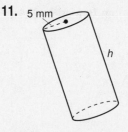

5 mm

h

$v = 1491.5$ mm^3

12.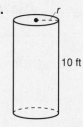

r

10 ft

$v = 196.25$ ft^3

13. Find the dimensions and volume of the largest cylinder that can be packed inside a box that has dimensions 14 in. by 7 in. by 2 in. Explain your reasoning. How much extra space would there be in the box?

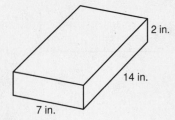

2 in.

14 in.

7 in.

14. A cylindrical fish tank 24 inches high has a base with a radius of 8 inches. You are filling the tank with water to a height of 22 inches. If the water is being pumped in at a rate of 2 cubic inches per second, how many minutes will it take to reach the desired level?

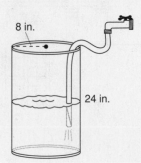

8 in.

24 in.

In Exercises 1–4, find the volume of the solid. Use 3.14 for π. Round your results to one decimal place.

1.
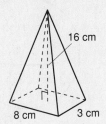
16 cm

8 cm   3 cm

2.
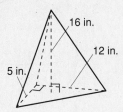
16 in.

12 in.

5 in.

3.
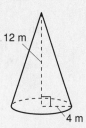
12 m

4 m

4.
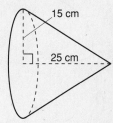
15 cm

25 cm

In Exercises 5 and 6, draw each solid and find its volume. Use 3.14 for π.

5. Pyramid with base 5 cm by 5 cm and height 3 cm

6. Cone with base radius 3 in. and height 4 in.

In Exercises 7–9, find the volume of the solid. Use 3.14 for π. Round your result to one decimal place.

7.
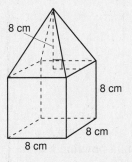
8 cm

8 cm

8 cm

8 cm

8.
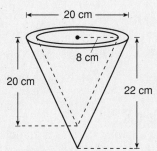
20 cm

8 cm

20 cm   22 cm

9.
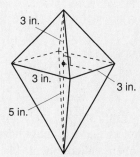
3 in.

3 in.   3 in.

5 in.

10. To complete a construction job, a contractor needs 145 more cubic yards of concrete. If there is a cone-shaped pile of concrete mix measuring 36 feet in diameter and 12 ft high on the job site, is there enough concrete to finish the job? Explain your result.

11. The limestone blocks from which an ancient pyramid was made weigh about 2 tons per cubic yard. Find the approximate weight of the pyramid having a square base of length 250 yards and a height of 150 yards. (Ignore tunnel and vault rooms.)

13. A jeweler is casting small gold cones for a special piece of jewelry. She has 60 g total of gold to use and wishes to make twelve cones with a radius of $\frac{1}{2}$ cm and a height of 1 cm. If gold weighs 19.32 grams per cubic centimeter, does she have enough gold to make the cones? Explain.

12.7

Name _____

In Exercises 1–4, find the volume of the sphere. Use 3.14 for π. Round results to 1 decimal place.

1.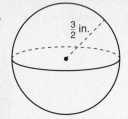
$\frac{3}{2}$ in.

2.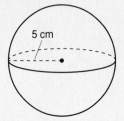
5 cm

3.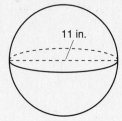
11 in.

4.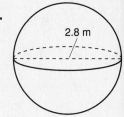
2.8 m

5. Find the volume of each planet in the table. Write results in scientific notation.

Planet	Diameter (in miles)	Volume
Earth	7,926	
Mercury	3,030	
Venus	7,520	
Mars	4,217	
Jupiter	88,700	
Saturn	74,975	
Uranus	32,200	
Neptune	30,800	
Pluto	1,423	

6. How many minutes will it take you to inflate a giant beach ball with a radius of 32 inches using a electric pump that can inflate a rate of 60 in.^{3}/sec?

7. A grain storage tank shown at the right is in the shape of a cylinder covered by a half sphere called a hemisphere. If the height of the cylinder is 50 feet and it is 80 feet in diameter, find the volume of the tank.

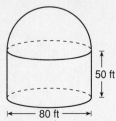
50 ft
80 ft

8. How much extra space will you have inside a cubicle box with dimensions 44 cm by 44 cm by 44 cm after placing a bowling ball in it with a radius of 21.8 cm?

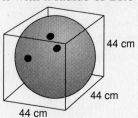
44 cm
44 cm
44 cm

In Exercises 9–11, complete the table. Leave your answers in terms of π.

	Radius of sphere	Diameter of sphere	Circumference of sphere at its "equator"	Volume of sphere
9.	10 mm	?	?	?
10.	?	?	36π in.	?
11.	?	?	?	$\frac{500}{3}\pi$ yd^3

12.8

Name _____

In Exercises 1–3, decide whether the solids are similar. If so, determine the scale factor of the shaded figure to the unshaded figure.

1.

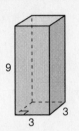

2.

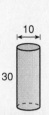

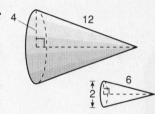

3.

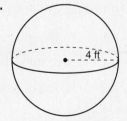

In Exercises 4–7, use the scale factor (of the given solid to a similar solid) to find the surface area and volume of the similar solid.

		Surface Area	Volume	Scale Factor of A to B
4.	Solid A	64 in.^{2}	28 in.^{3}	1:2
	Solid B	?	?	
5.	Solid A	?	?	2:1
	Solid B	608π in.^{2}	1920π in.^{3}	
6.	Solid A	36 cm^2	12 cm^3	?
	Solid B	324 cm^2	?	
7.	Solid A	108 ft^2	54 ft^3	2:3
	Solid B	?	?	

In Exercises 8–10, find the surface area and volume of the solid. Then use the scale factor to find the surface area and volume of a similar solid. Use 3.14 for π. Round to one decimal place.

8.

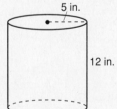

Scale factor 1:3

9.

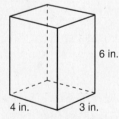

Scale factor 2:5

10.

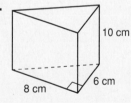

Scale factor 4:1

In Exercises 11–13, find the volume of the solid. Then use the scale factor to find the volume of a similar solid. Use 3.14 for π. Round to two decimal places.

11.

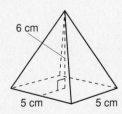

Scale factor 1:3

12.

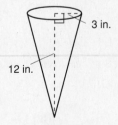

Scale factor 1:4

13.

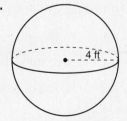

Scale factor 3:2

13.1

Name _____

In Exercises 1–3, decide whether the ordered pair is a solution of $2x - 3y = 4$.

1. $(-1, -2)$ **2.** $(5, -2)$ **3.** $\left(7, \frac{10}{3}\right)$

In Exercises 4–6, find several solutions of the linear equation. Use a table of values to organize your results.

4. $x - y = 4$ **5.** $3x + 4y = 12$ **6.** $y = -\frac{1}{2}x + 5$

In Exercises 7 and 8, use the table to decide whether the relationship between x and y is linear. Explain your reasoning.

7.

x	-3	-2	-1	0	1	2	3
y	-5	-1	3	7	11	15	19

8.

x	-3	-2	-1	0	1	2	3
y	9	6	3	0	-3	-6	-9

In Exercises 9 and 10, write the sentence as a linear equation. Then list several solutions.

9. The sum of 3 times a number and half another number is 10.

10. The difference of a number and 4 times another number is -12.

In Exercises 11–13, match the linear equation with the figure. Then list several solutions.

a. 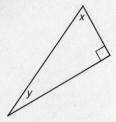   b. 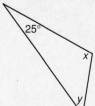   c.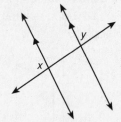

11. $x + y = 155$ **12.** $x + y = 180$ **13.** $x + y = 90$

In Exercises 14–17, use the following information.

For the years 1980 through 1994, a small college's enrollment can be modeled by the linear equation $N = 1500 + 60t$, where N is the enrollment and t is the year with $t = 0$ corresponding to 1980.

14. Determine the enrollment in 1987.

15. Determine the enrollment in 1994.

16. How many more students were enrolled each successive year?

17. Use the model to estimate the enrollment in 2000.

13.2

Name _____

In Exercises 1–3, match each equation with its graph.

a. 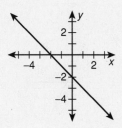   b. 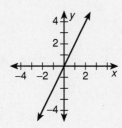   c.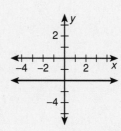

1. $y = 2x$

2. $y = -x - 2$

3. $y = -2$

In Exercises 4–7, decide whether the ordered pair is a solution to the equation. If not, find a solution.

4. $(2, 5)$; $2x - y = -1$

5. $(-1, 12)$; $y + 3x = 9$

6. $(4, 4)$; $3x - 2y + 4 = 0$

7. $(-5, -5)$; $x = -5$

In Exercises 8–11, sketch the graph of the equation.

8. $y = 2x + 1$

9. $y = 3x - 2$

10. $x = -1$

11. $y = \frac{1}{4}x$

In Exercises 12 and 13, graph both equations on the same coordinate plane. Then find the point of intersection of the two lines.

12. $x + y = 6$
$y = x + 2$

13. $y = 3x + 4$
$x + y = -4$

14. The point $(2, 8)$ lies on the graph of $y = cx + 2$. What is the value of c?

15. The point $(-2, 4)$ lies on the graph of $y = cx - 8$. What is the value of c?

16. The speed of sound decreases as the altitude increases. Given in the table is the altitude, h, in thousands of feet, and the speed of sound, v, in feet per second, at that altitude. Plot the data and describe the pattern. Is the pattern linear? Explain.

h	0	5	10	15	20	25	30	35
v	1116	1097	1077	1057	1036	1015	995	973

In Exercises 1–3, identify the intercepts of the graph.

1.
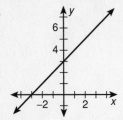

2.
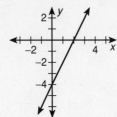

3.
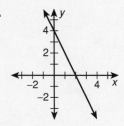

In Exercises 4–6, sketch a line having the given intercepts.

4. x-intercept: -2

y-intercept: 4

5. x-intercept: 1

y-intercept: -3

6. x-intercept: none

y-intercept: 2

In Exercises 7–10, match the equation with its graph.

a.
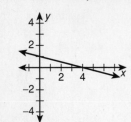

b.
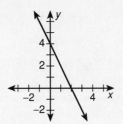

c.
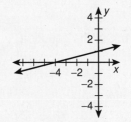

d.
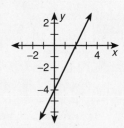

7. $2x + y = 4$

8. $2x - y = 4$

9. $y = \frac{1}{4}x + 1$

10. $y = -\frac{1}{4}x + 1$

In Exercises 11 and 12, use a calculator to find the intercepts of the line. Round your results to two decimal places.

11. $y = -2.15x + 4.25$

12. $y = 3.65x - 10.25$

13. The relationship between Fahrenheit temperature, F, and Celsius temperature, C, is given by the linear equation, $F = \frac{9}{5}C + 32$. Find the coordinates (C, F) of the intercepts of the graph and explain what they mean.

14. Your parents purchase a new automobile for $16,500. The value of the car depreciates linearly (at a constant rate). The value, V, of the car in terms of the number of years they own the car, t, is given by the equation, $V = 16500 - 1500t$. Find the coordinates (t, V) of the intercepts of the graph of the equation and explain what they mean.

In Exercises 1–3, determine whether a line with given slope rises to the right, falls to the right, is horizontal or is vertical.

1. $m = -\frac{1}{2}$ **2.** $m = 10$ **3.** $m = 0$

In Exercises 4 and 5, determine which slope is steeper.

4. $m = 3$, $m = \frac{7}{2}$, $m = 4$, $m = \frac{11}{3}$ **5.** $m = -6$, $m = -\frac{1}{2}$, $m = -4$, $m = 0$

In Exercises 6–8, find the slope of the line.

6.

7.

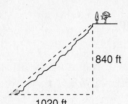

8.

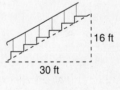

In Exercises 9–12, plot the points. Then find the slope of the line through the points.

9. $(2, 6), (-3, 4)$ **10.** $(0, 4), (-3, 0)$

11. $(-1, -2), (-3, -2)$ **12.** $(0, -6), (-2, -1)$

In Exercises 13–15, find the slope. Assume a left-to-right orientation.

13.

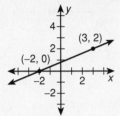

630 ft, 210 ft

14.

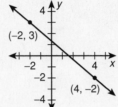

840 ft, 1020 ft

15.

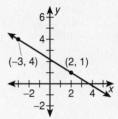

16 ft, 30 ft

In Exercises 16–18, find the slope of the hypotenuse.

16.

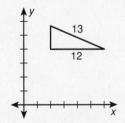

13, 12

17.

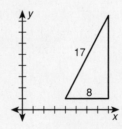

17, 8

18.

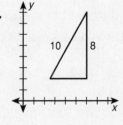

10, 8

In Exercises 19–22, find the slope of $\overleftrightarrow{MN}$ and $\overleftrightarrow{XY}$. Are the line parallel? Explain.

19. $M(0, 1), N(-1, -2), X(0, -6), Y(2, 0)$ **20.** $M(4, 8), N(-2, 5), X(2, -1), Y(-4, 2)$

21. $M(0, 1), N(-1, -4), X(5, 3), Y(-5, 1)$ **22.** $M(0, 6), N(3, 8), X(6, 2), Y(-3, -4)$

13.5

Name _____

In Exercises 1–6, find the slope and y-intercept of the line. Then sketch a quick graph of the line.

1. $y = 2x + 4$

2. $y = -\frac{1}{2}x + 2$

3. $y = 3x - 2$

4. $8y = -32x + 56$

5. $3x + 30y = 0$

6. $6x + 3y = 27$

In Exercises 7–10, match the equation with its graph.

a.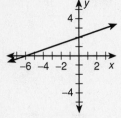

b.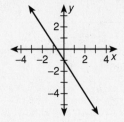

c.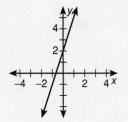

d.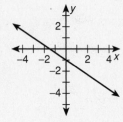

7. $y = 3x + 2$

8. $y = \frac{1}{3}x + 2$

9. $y = -\frac{2}{3}x - 1$

10. $y = -\frac{3}{2}x - 1$

In Exercises 11–14, decide whether the statement is true or false. Explain.

11. The line $3x - 9y = 12$ has a slope of 3 and a y-intercept of 4.

12. The line $10y = 2x - 70$ has a slope of $\frac{1}{5}$ and a y-intercept of -7.

13. The line $3x + 2y - 6 = 0$ rises to the right.

14. The line $6y = 2x$ rises to the right and passes through the origin.

In Exercises 15–18, use the following information.

For 1983 through 1989, the per capita consumption of chicken, C, in pounds, in the U.S. increased at a rate that was approximately linear. This relationship can be modeled by $C = 1.68t + 31.88$, when $t = 3$ represents 1983.

15. What is the slope and y-intercept of the consumption model?

16. How much more chicken was consumed each year?

17. Use the model to predict the per capita consumption in 1996.

18. Sketch a quick graph of the model.

In Exercises 19–21, write the equation of the line.

19.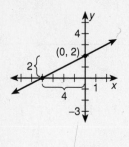

20.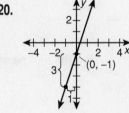

21.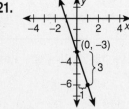

13.6

Name _____

1. Given in the table are the number of practice hours per week of 8 different golfers and their score on a par 72 golf course. Use a scatter plot to estimate the score of a golfer who practices 9 hours a week.

Golfer	1	2	3	4	5	6	7	8
Hours	2	4	5	6	8	10	5	7
Scores	90	85	80	78	72	67	82	76

2. Given in the table is the actual air temperature and the wind-chill factor at a wind speed of 10 mph. Use a scatter plot to estimate the wind-chill factor at an actual air temperature of 20°F and 10°F.

Actual Temperature	35°F	25°F	15°F	5°F	0°F	−5°F	−15°F
Wind-Chill Factor	22°F	10°F	−3°F	−15°F	−22°F	−27°F	−40°F

3. Each time you get dimes or quarters for change, you throw them into a jar. You have saved $50 in order to buy three new CD's that you want.

   a. Write a verbal and an algebraic model to represent the total saved.

   b. Create a table of values and graph the model.

   c. Interpret the intercepts of the graph in a real-life context.

4. A salesperson receives a 3% commission on sporting goods sold at a sale price and a 4% commission on sporting goods sold at the regular price. The salesperson earned a $250 commission.

   a. Write a verbal and an algebraic model to represent the total earned.

   b. Create a table of values and graph the model.

   c. Interpret the intercepts of the graph in a real-life context.

5. The winning times for the men's 100 meter freestyle in the Olympic Games for 1948-1988 are shown in the graph.

   a. What does this graph tell you about the winning times during this 44 year period?

   b. Describe the pattern. If this pattern were to continue, what would be the winning time in 1996?

   c. Do you think this pattern can continue for another 44 years? Explain.

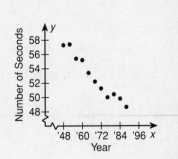

13.7

Name _____

In Exercises 1–6, determine if the ordered pair is a solution of the inequality.

1. $3x + y \geq 12$, $(4, 0)$ **2.** $5x - 6y < 30$, $(8, -1)$ **3.** $10x - 24y \leq 120$, $(6, -5)$

4. $y \leq -3x + 18$, $(7, -5)$ **5.** $y \geq 2x - 10$, $(12, 16)$ **6.** $2x - 8y > 16$, $\left(10, \frac{1}{4}\right)$

In Exercises 7–9, match the inequality with its graph.

a. 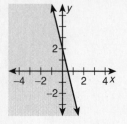   b. 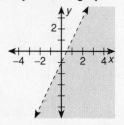   c.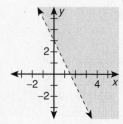

7. $y < 2x - 1$ **8.** $3y + 6x > 9$ **9.** $4x + y \leq 2$

In Exercises 10–12, graph the inequality. Then list several solutions.

10. $y \geq -\frac{1}{2}x + 4$ **11.** $y < -3x + 1$ **12.** $y \leq -3$

In Exercises 13–16, write an algebraic inequality that represents the statement.

13. The sum of the number of boys and twice the number of girls is less than 45.

14. The perimeter of a rectangular garden cannot exceed 400 feet.

15. The difference between the number of CD's and cassettes that you own is at least 42.

16. Joey and Paul of Joey and Paul's Painting have over 70 years of combined experience.

17. A bike company is introducing two new models. An all terrain model which sells for $625, and a racer model which sells for $500. You are the company's newest employee and your first assignment is to determine the number of models of each that must be sold in order to reach a sales goal of at least $25,000. Let a represent the all terrain model and r represent the racer model.

   a. Write the inequality that represents the situation.

   b. Graph the inequality.

   c. List three solutions of the inequality.

In Exercises 18–20, write an inequality whose solutions are given by the graph.

18. 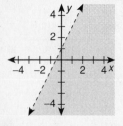   **19.** 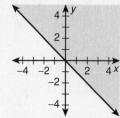   **20.**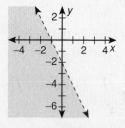

In Exercises 1–3, use the graph to estimate the distance between the points. Then use the Distance Formula to check your estimate.

1.

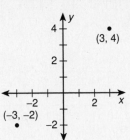

2.

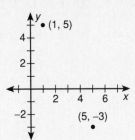

3.

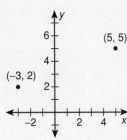

In Exercises 4–6, use the graph to estimate the midpoint of the two points. Then use the Midpoint Formula to check your estimate.

4.

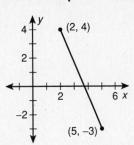

5.

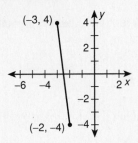

6.

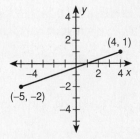

In Exercise 7, the labeled points are endpoints of a diameter of a circle. Find the center and radius of the circle.

In Exercise 8, show that parallelogram $WXYZ$ is a rectangle by proving that its diagonals are equal.

7.

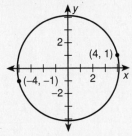

8.

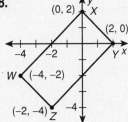

9. The map at the right is being used to plan a 26.3 mile marathon. Coordinates are given in miles. The locations of the participating towns on the map are: Curtis (0, 0), Clearfield (10, 2), Buster (5, 7), and Angel City (1, 4).

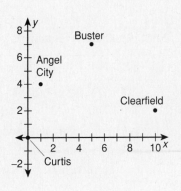

Which of the following planned routes is nearest to the 26.3 mile requirement?

   a. Curtis to Clearfield to Angel City to Curtis

   b. Curtis to Clearfield to Buster to Angel City to Curtis

   c. Curtis to Buster to Clearfield to Curtis

   d. Curtis to Buster to Angel City to Clearfield to Curtis

14.1

Name _____

In Exercises 1–4, find the mean, median, and mode of the data.

1. 30, 32, 31, 30, 29, 34

2. 16.5, 18.7, 19.2, 17.3, 18.4, 16.2, 17.6, 16.9

3. 7, 8, 10, 12, 6, 8, 9, 8, 9, 11, 9, 8, 12

4. 42, 48, 43, 48, 51, 51, 48, 46, 46

In Exercises 5–7, use the line plot at the right.

5. How many numbers are represented in the line plot?

6. Find the mean, median, and mode of the numbers.

7. Describe a real-life situation that can be represented by the line plot.

In Exercises 8–10, which measure of central tendency best represents the data? Explain your reasoning.

8. The favorite colors of 24 students from a second grade class.

9. The prices on a used car lot with a small number of very expensive cars.

10. The number of hours of study time each week by a college freshman.

In Exercises 11–13, use the picture graph, which shows the number of TV sets in each household on a particular street.

11. How many households have 3 TV's?

12. Find the mean, median, and mode number of TV's.

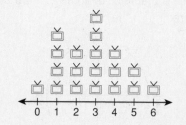

13. Which measure of central tendency best represents the number of TV's in a household? Explain.

In Exercises 14 and 15, the data in the table gives the prices of eight homes sold in a new housing development.

Home	1	2	3	4	5	6	7	8
Price	56,000	68,000	96,000	62,000	58,000	63,000	69,000	96,000

14. Find the mean, median, and mode of the data.

15. Which measure of central tendency best represents the data? Explain.

14.2

Name _____

1. List the data represented by the stem-and-leaf plot. Then draw a histogram for the data.

7	0 1 2 2 3
6	1 7 7 8
5	2 3 3 4
4	2 3
3	0

7|0 represents 70.

2. List the two sets of data represented by the double stem-and-leaf plot at the right.

5 5 3	3	8 8 9
9 8 7 6	2	0 1
	1	9

6|2|0 represents 2.6 and 2.0.

3. Draw a double bar graph to represent the data in the double stem-and-leaf plot.

4. The following data represents the ages of customers in a fast food restaurant on a particular Saturday between 11:00 A.M. and 1:00 P.M. Organize the data with an ordered stem-and-leaf plot.

24	33	39	51	16	18	24	28	33	53
12	13	16	25	35	60	37	27	51	20
32	36	47	41	26	28	17	19	23	39
25	29	34	39	43	51	53	62	60	19
17	23	20	30	33	36	49	42	47	50

In Exercises 5 and 6, use the set of data below which shows the batting averages of the American League Batting Champions for the years 1970 through 1993.

1970(.329)	1971(.337)	1972(.318)	1973(.350)	1974(.364)	1975(.359)	1976(.333)	1977(.388)
1978(.333)	1979(.333)	1980(.390)	1981(.336)	1982(.332)	1983(.361)	1984(.343)	1985(.368)
1986(.357)	1987(.363)	1988(.366)	1989(.339)	1990(.329)	1991(.341)	1992(.343)	1993(.363)

5. Organize the data in a stem-and-plot.

6. Draw a histogram to represent the data.

In Exercises 1–5, use the box-and-whisker plot. There are 20 numbers in the collection, and each number is different.

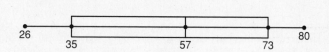

1. Name the smallest and largest numbers.

2. Name the first, second, and third quartiles.

3. What percent of the numbers are less than 29?

4. What percent of the numbers are greater than 29?

5. What percent of the numbers are between 18 and 40?

6. Draw a box-and-whisker plot of the data.
   4, 33, 99, 20, 79, 95, 22, 35, 93, 10 54, 85, 97,
   27, 12, 5, 72, 1, 42, 30

In Exercises 7 and 8, use the box and whisker plot which shows the average monthly high temperature distribution for Milwaukee, Wisconsin.

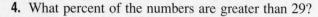

7. Write a description of Milwaukee's average monthly high temperature.

8. Create a box-and-whisker plot for Honolulu's average monthly high temperature in which the lowest monthly average high temperature is 80°, the highest is 88°, the first quartile is 81°, the median is 84.5°, and the third quartile is 87°.

In Exercises 9 and 10, use the data which lists the scores of the Super Bowl winning teams and the Super Bowl losing teams.

Winners: 35, 33, 16, 23, 16, 24, 14, 24, 16, 21, 32, 27, 35, 31, 27, 26, 27, 38, 38, 46, 39, 42, 20, 55, 20, 37, 52

Losers: 10, 14, 7, 7, 13, 3, 7, 7, 6, 17, 14, 10, 31, 19, 10, 21, 17, 9, 16, 10, 20, 10, 16, 10, 19, 24, 17

9. Using the same scale, create a box-and-whisker plot for both scores.

10. What do the plots tell you about the winning and losing scores? Write your answers in paragraph form.

11. List two different sets of numbers that could be represented by the box-and-whisker plot below. Describe a real-life situation that each set of your numbers could represent.

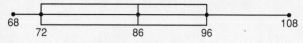

In Exercises 1–4, find the sum and difference of the matrices.

1. $\begin{bmatrix} 3 & -2 \\ 4 & 0 \end{bmatrix}, \begin{bmatrix} -3 & 7 \\ 5 & -3 \end{bmatrix}$

2. $\begin{bmatrix} 10 & 7 \\ -3 & 2 \end{bmatrix}, \begin{bmatrix} -5 & 2 \\ 9 & -1 \end{bmatrix}$

3. $\begin{bmatrix} 3 & 2 & -5 \\ 7 & 0 & 9 \end{bmatrix}, \begin{bmatrix} -2 & 0 & 5 \\ 10 & -3 & 2 \end{bmatrix}$

4. $\begin{bmatrix} 6 & 2 \\ -3 & 4 \\ 5 & -7 \end{bmatrix}, \begin{bmatrix} 9 & -8 \\ 6 & 4 \\ -3 & 2 \end{bmatrix}$

5. Use mental math to find a, b, c, and d.

$$\begin{bmatrix} 2a & -b \\ c+1 & \frac{1}{2}d \end{bmatrix} = \begin{bmatrix} 3 & -6 \\ 4 & 2 \end{bmatrix}$$

In Exercises 6 and 7, find two matrices whose sum is the given matrix. Do not use 0 as an element of either matrix.

6. $\begin{bmatrix} 3 & -2 \\ 4 & 6 \end{bmatrix}$

7. $\begin{bmatrix} 0 & 4 \\ -3 & 0 \end{bmatrix}$

In Exercises 8–11, use the following information.

You have opened two summer beach concession stands. The gross income for each stand for the three summer months is shown in the left table and the expenses are shown in the right table.

Gross Income	Stand 1	Stand 2
June	$635	$758
July	$785	$823
August	$815	$730

Expenses	Stand 1	Stand 2
June	$215	$295
July	$293	$320
August	$345	$292

8. Write each table as a matrix.

9. For each stand, which month has the greatest income?

10. Write a matrix which gives the monthly profit for each stand.

11. Which stand had a greater profit for the summer?

In Exercises 1–3, is the expression a polynomial? If it is, state whether it is a monomial, a binomial, or a trinomial.

1. $\sqrt{3}x^3 - 2x + 4$

2. $\frac{1}{2}x^2 - 4.2x$

3. $6x - \dfrac{2}{x^3} + 11$

In Exercises 4–6, match the algebra tiles with a polynomial. Then simplify the polynomial and sketch a rearranged version of the tiles that represent the simplified expression.

a.
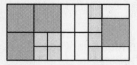

b.
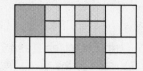

c.
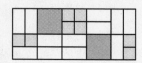

4. $x^2 + 5x + 2 + 4 + x^2 + 4x$

5. $5x + 2 + x^2 + 4 + 7x + x^2 + 2$

6. $3x^2 + 4 + 4x + 4 + 2x + x^2$

In Exercises 7–9, write the polynomial in standard form and list its terms.

7. $3z - 2z^3 + 14z^2$

8. $6x^4 - 2x + \frac{1}{2}x^2$

9. $10 - 2y - 3y^3$

In Exercises 10–13, simplify and write in standard form.

10. $3x - 2x^2 + 7x$

11. $z^4 - 3x^2 + z - 4z^2$

12. $5 - 4x^2 + 6 - 11x^2$

13. $\frac{4}{5}m^2 - 6 + 3m^2 - 11$

In Exercises 14–17, use the following information.

The Sears Tower in Chicago as of 1993 is the world tallest building. It's construction was completed in 1974. It is 110 stories high and measures 1454 feet in height. A penny is dropped from the top and its height, h, after t seconds is given by the equation $h = -16t^2 + 1454$.

14. Complete the table.

t	1	2	3	4	5	6	7	8	9	10
h										

15. What is the penny's height after 6 seconds?

16. When will the penny hit the ground?

17. If the penny was thrown upward with a velocity of 20 ft/sec the equation to model its height would be $h = -16t^2 + 20t + 1454$. Find its height after 10 seconds and 11 seconds. Explain your results.

14.6

Name _____

In Exercises 1 and 2, find and correct the error.

1.
$$\begin{array}{r} -4x^3 + 2x^2 \qquad -4 \\ + \qquad 3x^3 + 2x + 8 \\ \hline -4x^3 - x^2 + 2x + 4 \end{array}$$

2.
$$\begin{array}{r} 3x^3 + 2x^2 - 6x + 7 \\ -(2x^3 - 6x^2 - 4x - 8) \\ \hline x^3 - 4x^2 - 10x - 1 \end{array}$$

In Exercises 3 and 4, add or subtract the polynomials, as indicated. (Use a horizontal format.)

3. $(-3x^2 + 4x - 7) + (8x^2 - 3x - 3)$

4. $(-k^3 - 2k + 1) - (3k^2 - 4k - 11)$

In Exercises 5 and 6, add the polynomials. (Use a vertical format.)

5.
$$\begin{array}{r} w^3 - 3w^2 + 8w - 11 \\ + 3w^3 + 2w^2 - 10w - 7 \\ \hline \end{array}$$

6.
$$\begin{array}{r} 3d^4 - 3d^3 + 2d^2 - 16d - 11 \\ + -5d^4 + 2d^3 - 11d^2 + 10d - 7 \\ \hline \end{array}$$

In Exercises 7 and 8, subtract the polynomials. (Use a vertical format.)

7.
$$\begin{array}{r} 3x^3 - 2x^2 + 5x - 11 \\ - (-3x^3 + 11x^2 - 7x - 6) \\ \hline \end{array}$$

8.
$$\begin{array}{r} 2y^4 - 11y^3 - 2y^2 + 5y - 11 \\ - (-y^4 + 6y^3 + 11y^2 - 7y + 10) \\ \hline \end{array}$$

In Exercises 9–12, perform the indicated operations.

9. $(3x^2 - 7x + 5) + (-4x^2 - 6x + 11) + (x^2 - 3x + 7)$

10. $(-5k^2 - 11k + 10) + (3k^2 - 7k + 11) - (7k^2 - 4k + 3)$

11. $(-w^2 + 5) - (w^2 - 11w + 2) + (3w^2 - 11)$

12. $(4x^3 - 7x + 2) - (x^2 - 4x + 6) - (3x^3 - 2x^2 + 7x + 5)$

In Exercises 13 and 14, find the perimeter of the polygon. Then evaluate the perimeter when $x = 8$.

13.
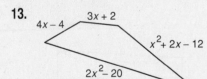

14.
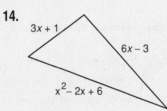

In Exercises 15 and 16, find an expression that represents the area of the unshaded region. Then evaluate the area when $x = 3$.

15.
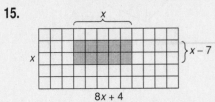

16.
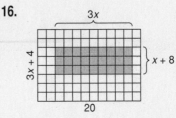

In Exercises 1–9, find the product.

1. $3x(4x^2 - 2)$

2. $-t^2(3t^3 + 2t - 3)$

3. $6w(w^4 - 3w^2 - 1)$

4. $12c^2(-c^2 + 2)$

5. $-3x(2x^3 - 2x^2 + 4x - 5)$

6. $-n^3(n^4 - 3n^3 + 2n^2 - 6)$

7. $z(7z^2 - 3z + 2)$

8. $-6k(3k^3 - 2k - 7)$

9. $-p^2(-3p^2 + 2p - 6)$

In Exercises 10–13, use the figure at the right.

10. Write an expression for the area of each region.

11. Use the result of Exercise 10 to write an expression for the area of the entire region.

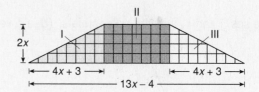

12. Use the formula for the area of a trapezoid to write an expression for the area of the entire region.

13. Compare the expressions obtained in Exercises 11 and 12.

In Exercises 14 and 15, translate the verbal phrase to an algebraic expression. Then simplify.

14. The product of a number, n, and three less than that number.

15. The square of a number, x, times the sum of twice the number and five.

In Exercises 16–19, use the prism at the right.

16. Write an expression for the area of the base.

17. Write an expression for the volume of the prism.

18. Write an expression for the surface area of the prism.

19. Evaluate your expressions for the volume and surface area when $x = 3$ cm.

1. Find and correct the error.

$$(3x + 5)(2x + 4) = (3x + 5)(2x) + (5)(2x + 4)$$
$$= 6x^2 + 10x + 10x + 20$$
$$= 6x^2 + 20x + 20$$

In Exercises 2–7, find the product using the Distributive Property.

2. $(x + 2)(5x + 1)$

3. $(3x + 4)(x + 5)$

4. $(2x + 7)(x + 4)$

5. $(4x + 2)(3x + 6)$

6. $(2x + 9)(x + 4)$

7. $(3x + 2)(5x + 3)$

In Exercises 8–10, multiply using a vertical format. Then check the results by using the Distributive Property.

8. $(3x + 9)(4x + 8)$

9. $(5x + 9)(4x + 11)$

10. $(6x + 10)(7x + 12)$

In Exercises 11–13, find the area of the figure.

11.

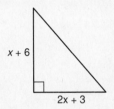

12.

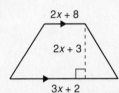

13.

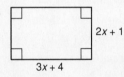

In Exercises 14 and 15 find the area of the shaded region.

14.

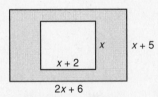

15.

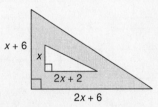

In Exercises 16 and 17, find the area of the mosaic made up of tiles by, first, writing its dimensions and, then, multiplying.

16.

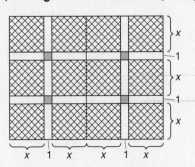

17.

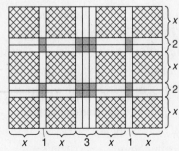

Answers to Exercises

■ Lesson 1.1

1. Add 4 to the preceding number; 18, 22, 26
2. Subtract 11 from the preceding number; 55, 44, 33
3. Divide the preceding number by 5; 25, 5, 1
4. Multiply the preceding number by 5; 1250, 6250, 31250
5. Multiply the preceding fraction by 2; $\frac{32}{3}$, $\frac{64}{3}$, $\frac{128}{3}$
6. Add $\frac{3}{2}$ to the preceding number; 9, $\frac{21}{2}$, 12
7. Add 1 to each preceding numerator and denominator; $\frac{6}{5}$, $\frac{7}{6}$, $\frac{8}{7}$
8. Multiply each preceding number by $n + 2$ starting with $n = 0$; 600, 3600, 25200
9. The pattern is every fourth letter of the alphabet; P, T, X
10. The pattern is every third letter of the alphabet; L, O, R
11. The pattern is every other letter of the alphabet starting with Z and working in reverse; T, R, P
12. The pattern is every other letter starting with B; J, L, N
13. 60, 54, 48, 42, 36, 30
14. 2, 3, 5, 8, 13, 21
15.

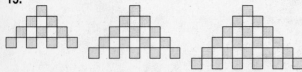

16.

17. The larger the number, the warmer the temperature. The smaller the number, the colder the temperature with 32°F representing the freezing temperature of water. Therefore, it was 70° warmer in Tempe than in Duluth.
18. The larger the number, the better the score with a score of 100 being a perfect score. So, your score is better than your friend's by 2 points.

19. The numbers represent the speed in miles per hour that you are traveling. The larger the number, the faster you are traveling. Therefore, you and your family will arrive at the beach much sooner than your friend and her family, since your family was traveling 320 mph faster than your friend's.
20. The numbers represent the points scored for a particular team. Because Dallas scored more than Buffalo, Dallas won the game.

■ Lesson 1.2

1. The quotient of 21 and 3 is 7.
2. The sum of 14 and 5 is 19.
3. The product of 42 and 3 is 126.
4. The difference of 133 and 17 is 116.
5. 178   **6.** 56   **7.** 995   **8.** 42.6
9. 94.4   **10.** 0.245   **11.** 4.07   **12.** 5.71
13. $\frac{7}{8}$ **14.** $\frac{7}{15}$ **15.** $\frac{6}{8} = \frac{3}{4}$ **16.** $\frac{1}{7}$
17. 112   **18.** 56   **19.** 352.6   **20.** 6
21. 2.5   **22.** 14.4   **23.** 14,074   **24.** 80.25
25. 114.375   **26.** 1445   **27.** 145
28. $\frac{42}{7} = 6$ **29.** $3 + 3 + 3 = 9$
30. $10 - 4 = 6$ **31.** $18 - 12 = 6$
32. $5 + 10 + 5 = 20$ **33.** 377,000
34. 6,293,200   **35.** $709,250

■ Lesson 1.3

1. 3 raised to the 4th power is 81.
2. The square root of 1.69 is 1.3.
3. 10.5^2; 110.25   **4.** 7^5; 16,807
5. 1.2^3; 1.728   **6.** 8.2^4; 4521.2176
7. $\left(\frac{2}{5}\right)^6$; $\frac{64}{15,625}$ **8.** $\left(\frac{1}{9}\right)^4$; $\frac{1}{6561}$
9. 25   **10.** 26   **11.** 15.6   **12.** 24.41
13. 2.74   **14.** 2.06   **15.** 9   **16.** 5
17. 5.8   **18.** 3.5   **19.** 144   **20.** 729
21. =   **22.** >   **23.** <   **24.** >
25. The perimeter of the kitchen is 80 ft. The perimeter of the bathroom is 32 ft. The area of the living room is 784 sq ft. The total area is 1248 sq ft.

26. a. 512 cubic inches
   b. 384 square inches
   c. Yes, if neither the length, width, nor height of the "smaller box" is greater than 8 in.

■ Lesson 1.4

1. 7   **2.** 15   **3.** 28   **4.** 0   **5.** 8

6. 41   **7.** 6   **8.** 6   **9.** 120   **10.** 16

11. 1   **12.** 30   **13.** 57   **14.** 17   **15.** 42.25

16. 57   **17.** 4   **18.** 8   **19.** 42

20. 192   **21.** 34   **22.** 129   **23.** True

24. False, $(18 - 6) \div 2 = 6$

25. False, $6 \cdot (3 - 2) \cdot 3 = 18$

26. False, $(24 - 3) \div 7 + 2 = 5$

27. False, $(5 + 2^2) \div 3 = 3$

28. True   **29.** False, $24 \div (4 + 2) - 2^2 = 0$

30. True   **31.** $36 \div (9 + 3) = 3$

32. $6 + (42 \div 21) = 8$ **33.** $42 \div (14 \div 2) = 6$

34. $12 - (4 \cdot 2) = 4$

35. Total cost = $4(5.25) + 4(1.25) + 4(1.15) + 3.75 + 3.00$ The total cost is \$37.35. The amount of money remaining is \$2.65.

■ Lesson 1.5

1. 4   **2.** 21   **3.** 6   **4.** 16   **5.** 14

6. 48   **7.** 4   **8.** 0   **9.** 16   **10.** 25

11. 4   **12.** 25   **13.** 3   **14.** 20   **15.** 16

16. 19   **17.** 49   **18.** 64   **19.** 54   **20.** 55

21. 23   **22.** 5   **23.** 3   **24.** 9   **25.** 3

26. 13   **27.** 9   **28.** 49   **29.** c   **30.** d

31. a   **32.** b   **33.** 2   **34.** 3

35. a. $8a + 6c$; **b.** \$112.00

36. a. 5 miles; **b.** 150 minutes

37. a. 255 yds; **b.** 765 ft; **c.** 114,750 sq ft

■ Lesson 1.6

1. Sister Act   **2.** \$41.4 million

3. \$307.5 million   **4.** University of Iowa

5. Yes, four more.

6. Yes, Iowa has dominated.

7. Answers vary.   **8.** March

9. ≈ 10.8 in.   **10.** ≈ 49.8 in.

11. No, the graph only shows the average monthly snowfall is very small, perhaps not measurable. But it does not state that it never snows during those months.

■ Lesson 1.7

1. Quadrilateral   **2.** Decagon

3. Hexagon   **4.** Octagon

5. It is not a polygon because not all its sides are straight.

6. It is a pentagon.

7. It is not a polygon because it has one more side than number of vertices.

8. It is an octagon.

9. Answers vary.   **10.** Answers vary.

11. An equilateral octagon

For Exercises 12–18, see following table.

Type of Polygon	No. of Sides	Sum/Int. Angles	Measure of an Int. Angle	No. of Vertices	Total No. Diagonals
12. Triangle	3	180°	60°	3	0
13. Octagon	8	1080°	135°	8	20
14. Nonagon	9	1260°	140°	9	27
15. Quadrilateral	4	360°	90°	4	2
16. Hexagon	6	720°	120°	6	9
17. Pentagon	5	540°	108°	5	5
18. Decagon	10	1440°	144°	10	35

19. Yes   **20.** No, no vertices, no straight edges

21. Yes   **22.** No, curved edges

■ Lesson 1.8

1.

n	0	1	2	3	4	5	6
$55n$	0	55	110	165	220	275	330

2.

n	1	2	3	4	5	6
$\frac{720}{n}$	720	360	240	180	144	120

3.

n	1	2	3	4	5	6	7	8	9
$\frac{n}{5}$	0.2	0.4	0.6	0.8	1.0	1.2	1.4	1.6	1.8

4.

n	1	2	3	4	5	6	7	8	9
$\frac{4}{n}$	4.0	2.0	$1.\overline{3}$	1.0	0.8	$0.\overline{6}$	$0.\overline{571428}$	0.5	$0.\overline{4}$

5.

n	1	2	3	4	5	6	7
$\frac{n+1}{n}$	2	1.5	$1.\overline{3}$	1.25	1.2	$1.1\overline{6}$	$1.\overline{142857}$

6.

n	0	1	2	3	4
$\frac{n(n+1)}{2}$	0	1	3	6	10

7. 6, 12, 18, 24, 30, 36, 42. Possible explanation: The sequence is the product of the first 7 natural numbers and 6, $6n$.

8. 102, 204, 306, 408, 510, 612, 714. Possible explanation: The three digit numbers can be determined by combining the first term as the first digit and twice the first term as the second and third digits.

9. [2] [+] [9] [=] [=] [=], 38, 47, 56, 65

10. [4] [×] [3] [=] [=] [=], 324, 972, 2916, 8748

11. [6] [×] [5] [=] [=] [=], 3750, 18750, 93750, 468750

12. [6144] [÷] [4] [=] [=] [=], 24, 6, 1.5, 0.375

13. 2500 **14.** 250000

15. 63001 **16.** 25010001

■ **Lesson 2.1**

1. 2 units by $x + 3$ units, $2(x + 3)$, $2x + 6$

2. 3 units by $2x + 4$ units, $3(2x + 4)$, $6x + 12$

3. $3x + 3$ **4.** $20x + 10$

 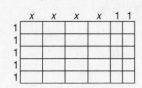

5. $6 + 10$ or 16   **6.** $48 + 84$ or 132

7. $3x + 6$ **8.** $15y + 60$ **9.** $4z + 12$

10. $16 + 8p$ **11.** $xy + 3x$ **12.** $ac + 4a$

13. $2x + 2y + 2z$ **14.** $az + 4z + bz$

15. $fg + 3f + fh$ **16.** $20 + 10y + 10z$

17. 30.8   **18.** 159.12   **19.** 20,251.5

20. a.
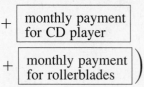

$$\boxed{\text{Total summer earnings}} = 16\left(\boxed{\substack{\text{Weekly earnings} \\ \text{job 1}}} + \boxed{\substack{\text{Weekly earnings} \\ \text{job 2}}}\right)$$

b. $\$1256 = 16(56 + 22.50)$

21. a. $\boxed{\text{Total}} = 12\left(\boxed{\substack{\text{monthly payment} \\ \text{for bike}}}\right.$

$+ \boxed{\substack{\text{monthly payment} \\ \text{for CD player}}}$

$+ \left.\boxed{\substack{\text{monthly payment} \\ \text{for rollerblades}}}\right)$

b. $\$783.00 = 12(26.50 + 21.25 + 17.50)$

■ **Lesson 2.2**

1. $4x$ **2.** $9y$ **3.** $8z + 10$

4. $9a + 5b$ **5.** $9z + 9$ **6.** $21z + 5$

7. $11s + 2t + 4$ **8.** $12x + 9y + 4$

9. $10x + 11$ **10.** $2a^2 + 10a$ **11.** $6z^2 + 7z$

12. $2x^3 + 2x^2$ **13.** $9y + 6$ **14.** $10z + 16$

15. $10st + 12$ **16.** $3x + 7z + 8$

17. $4x + 3y + 26$ **18.** $4ab + 2a + 4$

19. $9x + 2y, 35$ **20.** $3y + 4, 16$

21. $7x + 5y, 41$ **22.** $x^2 + xy + 3y, 33$

23. $2x^2 + xy, 30$ **24.** $5x + 5y, 35$

25. Perimeter $= 8x$

x	1	2	3	4	5
Perimeter	8	16	24	32	40

The perimeter increases by 8 each time x increases by 1.

26. Perimeter $= 12x$

x	1	2	3	4	5
Perimeter	12	24	36	48	60

The perimeter increases by 12 each time x increases by 1.

27. a. $x + 2y$
   b. $2x + 3y$
   c. $3x + 5y$
   d. $3(a + 1) + 5(b + 2) = 3a + 5b + 13$

■ Lesson 2.3

1. b   **2.** c   **3.** d   **4.** a

5. What number can be multiplied by 3 to obtain 36?; 12

6. 5 subtracted from what number is 3?; 8

7. $5 + x = 19$; 14   **8.** $\frac{x}{8} = 7$; 56

9. No, $x = 4$ **10.** Yes   **11.** Yes

12. No, $x = 4$ **13.** Yes, $4 = 4$

14. No, $4 \neq 20$

15. 5   **16.** 13   **17.** 24   **18.** 51

19. Conditional equation; true for $x = 12$.

20. Identity; true for all values of x.

21. 6.4 million   **22.** 5.4 million

23. 6.3 million

■ Lesson 2.4

1.
$$x + 21 = 65$$
$$x + 21 - 21 = 65 - 21$$
$$x = 44$$

2.
$$58 = y - 32$$
$$58 + 32 = y - 32 + 32$$
$$90 = y$$

3.
$$z - 28 = 101$$
$$z - 28 + 28 = 101 + 28$$
$$z = 129$$

4.
$$312 = w + 217$$
$$312 - 217 = w + 217 - 217$$
$$95 = w$$

5. 23   **6.** 54   **7.** 66   **8.** 618

9. 77   **10.** 14.9   **11.** 3.44   **12.** 8.7

13. 4.49   **14.** 62   **15.** 522.35   **16.** 10.229

17. 10.93   **18.** 97.02   **19.** 5418.08

20. $x - 7 = 28$; 35   **21.** $y + 2.7 = 8.3$; 5.6

22. $z + 3.1 = 15.2$; 12.1

23. $a - 5.01 = 22.7$; 27.71

24. 1713 yds   **25.** 1487 yds   **26.** 1690 yds

■ Lesson 2.5

1. The product of 5 and a number is 10; $x = 2$.

2. The quotient of a number and 2 is 11; $z = 22$.

3. 5   **4.** 10   **5.** 9   **6.** 5   **7.** 72

8. 20   **9.** 21   **10.** 60   **11.** 22   **12.** 2.6

13. 45   **14.** 33.75   **15.** 15.6   **16.** 45

17. 51.2   **18.** 48   **19.** 4   **20.** 3   **21.** 9

22. 6   **23.** 5748   **24.** 4840   **25.** 3857

26. 19,251   **27.** 4   **28.** 6   **29.** 17   **30.** 14

31. $5m = 45$, 9   **32.** $8c = 56$, 7

33. a.

Total yards	=	Yards per carry	·	Number of carries

b. $x = (4.368)(3838)$; $x = 16764.384$ yards
(NOTE: Actual total yards 16726.)

■ Lesson 2.6

1. a   **2.** c   **3.** b   **4.** d   **5.** $16 + n$

6. $\frac{n}{12}$ **7.** $\frac{n}{11}$ **8.** $8n$ **9.** $n - 12$

10. $6n + 14$ **11.** $8 - 5n$ **12.** $3n + 17$

13. $6(n + 4)$ **14.** $\frac{n}{m + 4}$ **15.** $3n - 6m$

16. $a + 5$ **17.** $a + 5$ **18.** $\frac{n}{4}$ **19.** $5c$

20. $a - 6$ **21.** $\frac{a}{3}$ or $\frac{1}{3}a$ **22.** $4a$ **23.** $a + 14$

24. a. $C = 38.70 + 5.75m$;   **b.** \$211.20

■ Lesson 2.7

1. d   **2.** b   **3.** a   **4.** c

5. $n - 5 = 13$, 18   **6.** $225.75 = 3x$, 75.25

7. $\frac{b}{7} = 9$, 63   **8.** $32 = 18 + y$, 14

9. The difference of a and 6 is 13.

10. 45 is the product of 5 and c.

11. The quotient of e and 5 is 40.

12. 15 is 3 more than f.

13. Verbal Model $\dfrac{\boxed{\text{Number}}}{\boxed{6}} = \boxed{21}$

Labels   Missing number $= x$

Algebraic Model $\dfrac{x}{6} = 21$

$$x = 126$$

14. Verbal Model

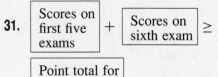

Labels   Missing number $= x$

Algebraic Model $165 = x \cdot 11$

$\qquad\qquad\qquad 15 = x$

15. Verbal Model

$$\boxed{\begin{array}{c}\text{Cost of items}\\\text{for you}\end{array}} + \boxed{\begin{array}{c}\text{Cost of item}\\\text{for your sister}\end{array}}$$

$$= \boxed{\begin{array}{c}\text{Total}\\\text{Cost}\end{array}}$$

Labels   Cost of items for you

$\qquad\qquad = 2.50 + 6.50 + 13.50$

$\qquad$ Cost of item for your sister $= x$

Algebraic Model $2.50 + 6.50 + 13.50 + x = 39.00$

$\qquad\qquad\qquad\qquad\qquad x = 16.50$

■ Lesson 2.8

1. $2 \cdot \left(\boxed{\text{Length}} + \boxed{\text{Width}} \right) = \boxed{\text{Perimeter}}$

2. Width $= w$

Length $= w + 48$

Perimeter $= 184$

3. $2 \cdot (w + 48 + w) = 184$ **4.** $w = 22$

5. Width is 22 ft and length is 70 feet.

6. $184 \cdot 5 = \$920$

7. $\boxed{\begin{array}{c}\text{Sales commission}\\\text{rate}\end{array}} \cdot \boxed{\begin{array}{c}\text{Monthly}\\\text{sales}\end{array}}$

$= \boxed{\begin{array}{c}\text{Sales}\\\text{commission}\end{array}}$

8. Sales commission rate $= \frac{1}{25}$;

Monthly sales $= 2600$

Sales commission $= x$

9. $\frac{1}{25} \cdot 2600 = x$ **10.** $x = 104$ **11.** $\$404$

12. 5 days per week $\times$ 2 trips per day $\times$ 16 miles per trip $= 160$ miles per week

13. 3 miles per day $\times$ 7 days per week $= 21$ miles per week

■ Lesson 2.9

1. Answers vary.   **2.** Answers vary.

3. Answers vary.   **4.** Answers vary.

5. Answers vary.   **6.** Answers vary.

7. $x < 5$ **8.** $y \geq 12$ **9.** $z < 5$

10. $a > 22$ **11.** $b < 10$ **12.** $27 > c$

13. $p < 15$ **14.** $q > 48.8$ **15.** $x < 9.7$

16. $294 > c$ **17.** $110.5 \geq y$ **18.** $2.8 < z$

19. $d - 5 \leq 4.25$, $d \leq 9.25$

20. $y + 7 > 10$, $y > 3$

21. $40x < 120$, $x < 3$ **22.** $69 > 3a$, $23 > a$

23. The difference of e and 4 is greater than 6.

24. The sum of 5 and f is less than or equal to 10.

25. 28 is less than the product of 7 and r.

26. The product of 17 and r is less than 102.

27. No   **28.** Yes   **29.** No   **30.** No

31.

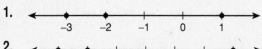

$\boxed{\begin{array}{c}\text{Scores on}\\\text{first five}\\\text{exams}\end{array}} + \boxed{\begin{array}{c}\text{Scores on}\\\text{sixth exam}\end{array}} \geq$

$\boxed{\begin{array}{c}\text{Point total for}\\\text{course to}\\\text{earn an A}\end{array}}$

32. $85 + 92 + 88 + 96 + 87 + x \geq 540$

33. $x \geq 92$

34. Yes, any test score greater than or equal to 92 would guarantee a point total greater than or equal to 540.

■ Lesson 3.1

1.

2.

3. $<$ **4.** $<$ **5.** $>$ **6.** $>$ **7.** $>$

8. $<$ **9.** $-3, 3$ **10.** $2, 2$ **11.** $-5, 5$

12. $6, 6$ **13.** $10, 10$ **14.** $100, 100$

15. 700 **16.** -57 **17.** 15 **18.** 20

19. $-6, -4, 2, 3, 5$ **20.** $-10, -7, 0, 6, 8$

21. $-3, -2, 1, 2, 4$ **22.** $-3, -1, 0, 1, 2$

23. 3 days   **24.** 9 days   **25.** 7 days

26. 3 days

27.

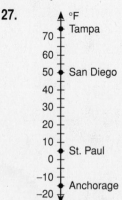

28. $70°$ **29.** $65°$

Lesson 3.2

1. $3 + 12 = 15$ 2. $-6 + (-3) = -9$
3. $-12 + (-12) = -24$ 4. $6 + 16 = 22$
5. $-5 + 5 = 0$ 6. $12 + (-18) = -6$
7. $-19 + 12 = -7$ 8. $26 + (-26) = 0$
9. $4 + 0 = 4$ 10. $0 + (-11) = -11$
11. $15 + (-2) = 13$ 12. $-12 + 0 = -12$
13. 2, 3, 4, 5, 6 The numbers increase by 1.
14. $0, -1, -2, -3, -4$
    The numbers decrease by 1.
15. $-4, -2, 0, 2, 4$ The numbers increase by 2.
16. Answers vary.   17. Answers vary.
18. Answers vary.   19. $x = -9$
20. $z = 2$ 21. $m = 13$
22. b, $x = -70$, 70 feet below sea level
23. a, $x = 70$, $70 in the account
24. Answers vary.   25. Answers vary.
26. b, c   27. a, c

Lesson 3.3

1. $6 + (-2) + (-8) = -4$
2. $-6 + (-2) + 10 = 2$
3. $6 + (-7) + (-8) = -9$
4. $-16 + 15 + (-3) = -4$
5. $-10 + 11 + (-2) = -1$
6. $-10 + 6 + (-8) = -12$
7. $-10 + (-6) + (-15) = -31$
8. $6 + (-5) + (-4) = -3$
9. $10 + (-2) + 13 = 21$
10. -65 11. 155   12. -342 13. -47
14. Negative, $|-321| > |215 + 43|$
15. Positive, $|115| > |-38 + (-42)|$
16. $2x, 6$ 17. $11x + 4, 37$ 18. $2x, 6$
19. $9x + 10, 37$ 20. $5x + 7, 22$
21. $8x + 6, 30$ 22. $x, 3$ 23. $6x + 8, 26$
24. $19x + 4, 61$ 25. $5x + 11, 26$
26. $>$ 27. $>$ 28. $<$ 29. $<$ 30. $<$
31. $>$ 32. $5/share   33. 50th floor

Lesson 3.4

1. $3 - 7 = -4$ 2. $-4 - (-3) = -1$
3. $6 - (-8) = 14$ 4. $10 - (-2) = 12$
5. $-23 - 2 = -25$ 6. $12 - (-8) = 20$
7. $14 - (-3) = 17$ 8. $16 - (-16) = 32$
9. $-16 - 16 = -32$ 10. $-1, -5$
11. 1, 5   12. $0, -4$ 13. 4, 8   14. 0, 0
15. $4, -4$ 16. $4x + (-2x) + 8; 4x, -2x, 8$
17. $10x + (-12) + (-5); 10x, -12, -5$
18. $-6x - 7$ 19. $9m + 2$ 20. $-9y - 3$
21. $-58x$ 22. $12z$ 23. $6 - m$ or $-m + 6$
24. 24   25. 209   26. 6   27. -6
28. Answers vary.   29. Answers vary.
30. Asia   30,340 ft
    North America 20,602 ft
    Africa   19,852 ft
    Europe   18,602 ft
31. -1030 ft   32. 830 ft

Lesson 3.5

1. $6 \cdot 5 = 30$ 2. $8(10) = 80$
3. $-3 \cdot (-2) = 6$ 4. $-15 \cdot 3 = -45$
5. $10 \cdot (-3) = -30$ 6. $7 \cdot (-4) = -28$
7. $(-3)(-7) = 21$ 8. $(0)(-30) = 0$
9. $(4)(0) = 0$ 10. $8y$ 11. $-10a$
12. $11w$ 13. -12 14. -36 15. 4
16. -12 17. 60   18. -30 19. 24
20. 30   21. 36   22. 351   23. -4242
24. 3978   25. -40 26. -99
27. 1806   28. -9 29. -5 30. -10
31. 3   32. -12 33. 5   34. -8
35. -4 36. -16 37. 41°F, 14°F

Lesson 3.6

1. 32   2. 45   3. -32 4. 26
5. -18 6. 0   7. 0   8. 48   9. -42
10. $-18, -17, -16, -15, -14$
    The numbers increase by 1.
11. 2, 3, 4, 5, 6; The numbers increase by 1.
12. 12   13. 4   14. 6   15. -16 16. 20
17. -18 18. -22 19. -30 20. -30
21. 15   22. -6 23. 55.755 seconds
24. Less than result in Exercise 23. If trend of
    faster times continues, then the average of
    the next six Olympic games will be faster.

■ Lesson 3.7

1. Yes   **2.** No, $y = -4$

3. Yes   **4.** No, $m = -48$

5. 3   **6.** -3 **7.** 17   **8.** -9

9. -10 **10.** -8 **11.** -3 **12.** 16

13. 33   **14.** 2   **15.** -3 **16.** -16

17. $x + 3 = -6$, $x = -9$
The sum of -9 and 3 is -6.

18. $-3z = -27$, $z = 9$
The product of 9 and -3 is -27.

19. -2556 **20.** 4080   **21.** 36   **22.** -1334

23. -528 **24.** 253   **25.** c   **26.** a   **27.** b

28. d   **29.** f   **30.** e   **31.** $72 = 32t$

32. $t = 2.25$ hours (2 hours 15 minutes)

■ Lesson 3.8

1. S, 3   **2.** Q, 1   **3.** R, 4   **4.** P, 2

5. U, 2   **6.** T, 3   **7.** 4   **8.** 1   **9.** 3

10. 2   **11.** 2   **12.** 1   **13.** 3   **14.** 4

15. 3 units^2; 8 units   **16.** 36 units^2; 26 units

17. $2 + (-12) = -10$; Answers vary.

18. $9 - 3 = 6$; Answers vary.

19. $12 - 2 = 10$; Answers vary.

20. $17,500   **21.** $10,000

22. $V = 25000 - 2500t$ **23.** Answers vary.

■ Lesson 4.1

1. 9   **2.** 3   **3.** -1 **4.** 8   **5.** -15

6. -25 **7.** 36   **8.** 2   **9.** 3

10.

11. $2x + 3 = 13$; 5   **12.** $6x + 11 = 65$; 9

13. $\frac{x}{3} + 2 = -7$; -27 **14.** $\frac{x}{4} - 6 = 1$; 28

15. $2x + 17 = 43$; 13   **16.** $4x + 34 = 94$; 15

17. a. $\boxed{\text{Length}} = 2 \cdot \boxed{\text{width}} + \boxed{\text{six feet}}$

b. Length = 78 feet
Width = w

c. $78 = 2w + 6$
$w = 36$

d. The width is 36 feet.

18. Answers vary.

■ Lesson 4.2

1. No; $x = 2$ **2.** No; $y = -2$ **3.** Yes

4. Yes   **5.** -4 **6.** 12   **7.** -16 **8.** 11

9. -13 **10.** 2   **11.** -9 **12.** 13   **13.** -6

14. $2x + 5x + (-3x) + (-3) = 9$; 3

15. $7y + 2y - 11 = -38$; -3

16. $10x - 10 + 4x + 8 = 180$;
$x = 13$; $120°, 60°$

17. $22x - 2 + 15x + 18x + 2 + 5x = 360$;
$x = 6$; $130°, 90°, 110°, 30°$

18. a. $(8 + 7 + 7 + 4 + 7 + 10 + 10)x = 323.30$

b. $x = 6.10$; $6.10 per hour

■ Lesson 4.3

1. Divide both sides of the equation by 4 or multiply both sides by $\frac{1}{4}$.

2. Divide both sides of the equation by -3 or multiply both sides by $-\frac{1}{3}$.

3. 10   **4.** -15 **5.** 20   **6.** 18

7. 4   **8.** $-\frac{4}{3}$ **9.** 2   **10.** 10

11. 7   **12.** 10   **13.** -9 **14.** -8

15. $4n + 16 = 100$; $n = 21$

16. $3n - 23 = 34$; $n = 19$

17. $\frac{1}{2}n + 27 = 40$; $n = 26$

18. $13 = \frac{1}{5}n - 8$; $n = 105$ **19.** 75 cm

20. a.

$2w + 6$

w

b. Width = 11 inches
Length = 28 inches

21. Arkansas' governor salary = $35,000
New York's governor salary = $130,000

■ Lesson 4.4

1. The second line should be $-3x + 2 = 8$; $x = -2$

2. The second line should be $4x - 8 + 6 = 16$; $x = \frac{9}{2}$ or 4.5

3. 2   **4.** 4   **5.** 5   **6.** -2 **7.** 2

8. 3   **9.** -30 **10.** -34 **11.** -8

12. a. -20 **13. a.** -3
   b. -20 **b.** -3
   c. Answers vary.   **c.** Answers vary.

14. $6(x + 5) = 42$; $x = 2$

15. $(3x - 2) + (2x - 1) + (7x + 3) = 180$; $x = 15$; $43°$, $29°$, $108°$

16. $7(x) + 3(9) = 5(9 + x)$; $x = 9$; 9 pounds of cashews

■ Lesson 4.5

1. c   **2.** a   **3.** b   **4.** -6

5. 1   **6.** -4 **7.** -6 **8.** -31

9. -8 **10.** $-\frac{5}{3}$ **11.** 2   **12.** -2

13. $3x + 14 = x + 20$; $x = 3$

14. $5x + 38 = 2x + 47$; $x = 3$

15. $4x - 2 = 3x + 2$; $x = 4$

16. $4(x + 3) = 2x + 8$; $x = -2$

17. $x = 4$; the perimeter is 36 units.

18. $x = 6$; the length of the each side is 20 units.

19. $x + 18 + 10 = 2(x + 10)$; $x = 8$
The second culture is 8 days old. The first culture is 26 days old.

■ Lesson 4.6

1. Students' tables and graphs may vary slightly.

Minutes	1	2	3	4	5
Company 1	2.00	2.15	2.30	2.45	2.60
Company 2	2.50	2.60	2.70	2.80	2.90

Minutes	6	7	8	9	10
Company 1	2.75	2.90	3.05	3.20	3.35
Company 2	3.00	3.10	3.20	3.30	3.40

Minutes	11	12	13	14	15
Company 1	3.50	3.65	3.80	3.95	4.10
Company 2	3.50	3.60	3.70	3.80	3.90

1. —CONTINUED—

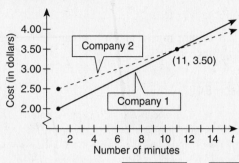

2.

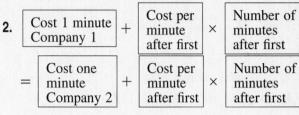

3. Cost first minute Company 1 = \$2.00
Cost per minute after first = \$0.15
Number of minutes after first = $t - 1$
Cost first minute Company 2 = \$2.50
Cost per minute after first = \$0.10
Number of minutes after first = $t - 1$

4. $2 + 0.15(t - 1) = 2.50 + 0.10(t - 1)$

5. $t = 11$ **6.** 11 minutes   **7.** \$3.50

8. $2500 + 12x = 52x$; $x = 62.5$; so you need to sell at least 63 helmets to break even.

■ Lesson 4.7

1. The second line should be $5.5x + 11.25 = 22.5$; $x \approx 2.05$

2. The second line should be $0.8575x - 2.037 = 12.64$; $x \approx 17.12$

3. -3.5 **4.** 1.08   **5.** 1.12   **6.** 1.67

7. 1.58   **8.** 1.22   **9.** -21.58 **10.** 2.62

11. -5.27 **12.** 7.96   **13.** 5.67   **14.** 12.24

15. 1.39   **16.** 0.72   **17.** \$25.65   **18.** \$5.65

19. 29 wings (total bill \$4.98)

20. ≈ 56.78 miles or 57 miles

■ Lesson 4.8

1. 8; each side is 6 units.

2. 4; width is 22 units; length is 10 units.

3. $x = 3$; each side is 13 units.

4. $x = 25$; $m\angle 1 = 70°$, $m\angle 2 = 110°$

5. $x = 14$; $m\angle 1 = 45°$, $m\angle 2 = 50°$, $m\angle 3 = 85°$

6. 1836 square feet   **7.** 52 square inches

8. 12,636 square feet

9. 53,125 square miles; area of rectangle + area of triangle.

■ Lesson 5.1

1.

2. 5 seasons   **3.** 33 seasons

4. 5 seasons (as of 1994)

5. There would be half as many TV's in each row.

6. 25 years   **7.** ≈ 1803

8. Periodic table of elements introduced.

9. Boyle's Law formulated.

■ Lesson 5.2

1. A simple bar graph, one bar could be used for each type of blood.

2. A double bar graph or stacked bar graph

3. 1901-10

4. 1921 to 1930 and 1931 to 1940

5. Yes, it appears that during the twentieth century, the number of immigrants was at the highest from 1901–1910. Then the number decreased, reaching its lowest from 1931–1940. Since then it appears the number of immigrants increases each decade.

6. If the trend continues there should be more than 8000 immigrants from 1991-2000.

7. See students' graphs. Time intervals may vary. One possible graph:

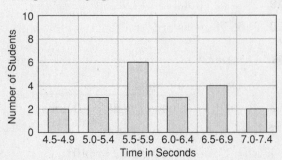

■ Lesson 5.3

1. The units of the horizontal axis are years starting with 1980 increasing in increments of one year. The units of the vertical axis are number of tornadoes starting with 0 increasing in increments of 100.

2. ≈ 1050

3. 1981, 1983, 1984, 1985, and 1987

4. Many possible theories:

1. greenhouse effect causing more severe weather
2. better reporting of data

5.

Width	2	2	2	2	2
Length	2	3	4	5	6
Perimeter	8	10	12	14	16

6.

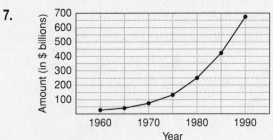

7.

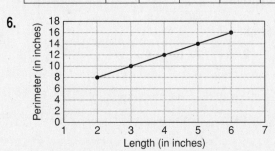

8. Answers vary.

■ Lesson 5.4

1. A picture graph or bar graph would be best for simple data. Possible graph:

Country	Number of Travelers (in millions)
Canada	🏃🏃🏃🏃🏃🏃🏃🏃🏃🏃🏃🏃
Europe	🏃🏃🏃🏃🏃🏃🏃
Mexico	🏃🏃🏃🏃🏃🏃
Latin America	🏃🏃
Other	🏃🏃🏃🏃🏃🏃

🏃 = 1 million travelers

2. a. ≈ 7.5 million (7.4)

  b. Walking, swimming, aerobics

  c. Walking

  d. Possibly a double bar graph if you want to compare men and women in each activity and not necessarily the total of each activity.

3. A time line is the best way to present the data.

■ Lesson 5.5

1. The consumption of pork appears to be 7 times as much as that of fish.

2. The consumption of pork is only about 3 times as much as that of fish.

3. Yes, because the vertical scale starts at 12 instead of 0.

4.

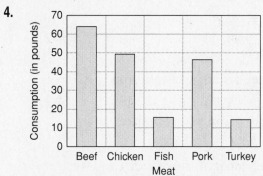

5. July's bill appears to be twice June's bill.

6. July's bill is $85 and June's $65. July's is only $20 more than June's.

7. The vertical scale is misleading because the units start at $50.

8.

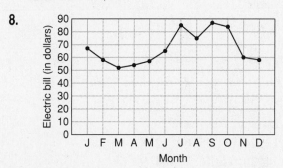

■ Lesson 5.6

1. Yes. Explanations vary.

2. Yes. Explanations vary.

3.

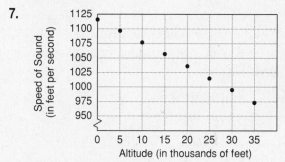

4. a. 1 hit per game; **b.** 0.250 batting average

■ Lesson 5.7

1. No correlation. Answers vary.

2. Negative correlation. Answers vary.

3. Positive correlation. Answers vary.

4. Positive correlation. As the number of study hours increases, test scores should increase.

5. No correlation. The number of pets you own and your age have no pattern.

6. Negative correlation. As the number of hours you watch TV increase, test scores should decrease.

7.

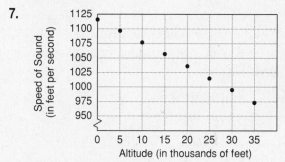

8. Negative correlation

9. About 1065 ft/sec

10. About 27,000 feet

11. About 10.9 million

12. Positive correlation. As the years go by, the enrollment increases.

13. Answers will vary slightly. In 1995, the enrollment should be about 11.7 million.

■ Lesson 5.8

1. $\frac{1}{6}$ **2.** $\frac{1}{2}$ **3.** $\frac{1}{3}$ **4.** $\frac{2}{3}$ **5.** $\frac{1}{2}$

6. $\frac{1}{3}$ **7.** $\frac{1}{13}$ **8.** $\frac{3}{13}$ **9.** $\frac{3}{26}$ **10.** $\frac{2}{13}$

11. 5 blue socks, 10 white socks, 4 black socks and 1 argyle sock

12. a. $\frac{614}{3577}$ or ≈ 0.17

  b. $\frac{444}{3577}$ or ≈ 0.12

13. $\frac{1148}{3577}$ or ≈ 0.32 **14.** $\frac{2429}{3577}$ or ≈ 0.68

■ Lesson 6.1

1. Yes: 2, 3, 4, 6, and 8; No: 5, 7, 9, and 10

2. Yes: 3, 5, 7, and 9; No: 2, 4, 6, and 10

3. Yes: 2, 3, 4, 5, 6, 8, 9, and 10; No: 7

4. Yes: 2, 3, 4, 6, 8 and 9; No: 5, 7, and 10

5. Yes: 2, 3, 6, and 9; No: 4, 5, 7, and 10

6. Yes: 3, 5, 7, and 9; No: 2, 4, 6, 8, and 10

7. 8   **8.** 1, 3, 5, 7, or 9

9. 1, 4, or 7   **10.** 0 or 6

11. 0, 1, 2, 3, 4, 5, 6, 7, 8, or 9

12. 315   **13.** 24

14. Let $a = 4x$ and $b = 4y$, and let x and y be integers. Then
  a. $a + b = 4x + 4y = 4(x + y)$
  b. $a - b = 4x - 4y = 4(x - y)$
  c. $ab = (4x)(4y)$
  d. $\dfrac{a}{b} = \dfrac{4x}{4y} = \dfrac{x}{y}$

In **a**, **b**, and **c**, x and y can still be integers so that the expressions are always divisible by 4. In **d**, $\frac{x}{y}$ may be a fraction or an integer not divisible by 4.

15. 1, 2, 3, 4, 6, 8, 12, 24

16. 1, 2, 3, 6, 9, 18, 27, 54

17. 1, 2, 3, 4, 6, 8, 12, 16, 24, 48

18. 1, 3, 5, 7, 15, 21, 35, 105

19. 1 mi-by-80 mi, 2 mi-by-40 mi, 4 mi-by-20 mi, 8 mi-by-10 mi, 16 mi-by-5 mi

20. 20 yd-by-20 yd

■ Lesson 6.2

1. Composite, $39 = 13 \cdot 3$

2. Prime, $41 = 41 \cdot 1$ only

3. Composite, $57 = 19 \cdot 3$

4. $2^4 \cdot 3$ **5.** 3^3 **6.** $2 \cdot 3^3$

7. $2 \cdot 3 \cdot 7$ **8.** 2^6 **9.** $2^2 \cdot 3 \cdot 7$

10. $2^4 \cdot 3^2$ **11.** $2^3 \cdot 5^2$ **12.** $2^2 \cdot 3^2 \cdot 5$

13. $(-1) \cdot 2 \cdot 2 \cdot 3 \cdot 3$; $(-1) \cdot 2^3 \cdot 3^2$

14. $(-1) \cdot 3 \cdot 3 \cdot 5$; $(-1) \cdot 3^2 \cdot 5$

15. $2 \cdot 2 \cdot 2 \cdot 3 \cdot x \cdot x$; $2^3 \cdot 3 \cdot x^2$

16. $2 \cdot 2 \cdot 2 \cdot 2 \cdot a \cdot a \cdot a \cdot b \cdot b$, $2^4 \cdot a^3 \cdot b^2$

17. 90   **18.** 336   **19.** -540

20. 1, 2, 4, 8, 16   **21.** 1, 2, 3, 4, 6, 8, 12, 24

22. 1, 2, 3, 6, 9, 18, 27, 54

23. 5, 13, 17, 29, 37, 41, 53, 61, 73, 89, 97
$5 = 4 + 1$, $13 = 9 + 4$, $17 = 16 + 1$,
$29 = 25 + 4$, $37 = 36 + 1$, $41 = 25 + 16$,
$53 = 49 + 4$, $61 = 36 + 25$, $73 = 64 + 9$,
$89 = 64 + 25$, $97 = 81 + 16$

24. No other pairs exist because for a pair of numbers to be consecutive one must be even therefore composite.

■ Lesson 6.3

1. 6   **2.** 6   **3.** 10   **4.** 18   **5.** 240

6. 165   **7.** $2xy$ **8.** $2xy^2$ **9.** $5r^2p$

10. $9x^2y^3$ **11.** 10 and 15, 20 and 25, ...

12. 3 and 6, 9 and 12, ...

13. 12 and 24, 36 and 48, ...

14. Yes   **15.** No, GCF = 3   **16.** Yes

17. $A = 28$, $P = 22$
They are not relatively prime, GCF = 2.

18. $A = 108$, $P = 42$
They are not relatively prime, GCF = 6.

19. $A = 77$, $P = 36$
They are relatively prime.

20. GCF = 2   **21.** GCF = 3

22. 7 children; A can of soda costs $0.48 and one candy bar costs $0.35.

■ Lesson 6.4

1. 5, 10, 15, 20, 25, 30, 35, 40, ...
7, 14, 21, 28, 35, 42, 49, ...
LCM = 35.

2. 3, 6, 9, 12, 15, 18, 21, 24, 27, ...
8, 16, 24, 32, ...
LCM = 24.

3. 9, 18, 27, 36, 45, ...
12, 24, 36, 48, ...
LCM = 36.

4. 12, 24, 36, 48, 60, 72, 84, 96, ...
14, 28, 42, 56, 70, 84, 98, ...
LCM = 84.

5. 3, 6, 9, 12, 15, 18, 21, 24, 27, 30, 33, ...
5, 10, 15, 20, 25, 30, 35, ...
6, 12, 18, 24, 30, 36, ...
LCM = 30.

6. 5, 10, 15, 20, 25, 30, 35, 40, 45, 50, 55, 60, 65, ...
   6, 12, 28, 24, 30, 36, 42, 48, 54, 60, 66, ...
   12, 24, 36, 48, 60, 72, ...
   LCM = 60.

7. $36 = 2 \cdot 2 \cdot 3 \cdot 3, 54 = 2 \cdot 3 \cdot 3 \cdot 3$
   LCM $= 2 \cdot 2 \cdot 3 \cdot 3 \cdot 3 = 108$

8. $15 = 3 \cdot 5, 35 = 5 \cdot 7$
   LCM $= 3 \cdot 5 \cdot 7 = 105$

9. $145 = 5 \cdot 29, 275 = 5 \cdot 5 \cdot 11$
   LCM $= 5 \cdot 5 \cdot 11 \cdot 29 = 7975$

10. $81 = 3 \cdot 3 \cdot 3 \cdot 3, 216 = 2 \cdot 2 \cdot 2 \cdot 3 \cdot 3 \cdot 3$
    LCM $= 2 \cdot 2 \cdot 2 \cdot 3 \cdot 3 \cdot 3 \cdot 3 = 648$

11. $13xy^2 = 13 \cdot x \cdot y \cdot y$,
    $26x^2y^3 = 2 \cdot 13 \cdot x \cdot x \cdot y \cdot y \cdot y$
    LCM $= 2 \cdot 13 \cdot x \cdot x \cdot y \cdot y \cdot y = 26x^2y^3$

12. $3x^2 = 3 \cdot x \cdot x, 5y^2 = 5 \cdot y \cdot y$
    LCM $= 3 \cdot 5 \cdot x \cdot x \cdot y \cdot y = 15x^2y^2$

13. 3 and 13

14. Possible answers: 4 and 9, 4 and 18, 12 and 18

15. 4 and 25

16. Possible answers: 8 and 18 or 18 and 24

17. 75 bottles, 4 packs

18. 352 miles; Angel's car used 11 gallons. Mo's car used 16 gallons.

19. 84 minutes later at 2:24 A.M.

■ **Lesson 6.5**

1. $4, \frac{3}{7}$ 2. $4, \frac{2}{9}$ 3. $9, \frac{1}{5}$ 4. $11, \frac{2}{7}$

5. $2, \frac{2}{19}$ 6. $12, \frac{7}{9}$ 7. $\frac{1}{3y}$ 8. $\frac{b}{4a}$

9. $\frac{1}{3z^3}$ 10. $\frac{8yz}{9}$ 11. $\frac{3x^2}{5y^4}$ 12. $\frac{2x}{5y^2}$

13. $\frac{9}{16}$ 14. $\frac{7}{12}, \frac{4}{49}$ 15. $\frac{9}{64}, \frac{15}{20}$ 16. $\frac{25}{64}$

17. Possible answers: $\frac{8}{10}, \frac{12}{15}$, and $\frac{16}{20}$

18. Possible answers: $\frac{14}{16}, \frac{21}{24}$, and $\frac{28}{32}$

19. Possible answers: $\frac{1}{3}, \frac{2}{6}$, and $\frac{3}{9}$

20. >   21. =   22. <   23. =

24. >   25. =   26. $\frac{1}{11}$ 27. $\frac{2}{11}$

28. Mr. Morgan's class did better because $\frac{24}{36} > \frac{21}{35}$.

■ **Lesson 6.6**

1. $-\frac{3}{1}$ 2. $\frac{11}{20}$ 3. $\frac{9}{25}$

4. $\frac{32}{3}$ 5. $-\frac{17}{5}$ 6. $\frac{67}{4}$

7. Rational, $0.\overline{36}$, repeating

8. Rational, 0.625, terminating

9. Rational, 4, terminating

10. Irrational, 5.6568542..., non-repeating

11. Rational, 0.5625, terminating

12. Rational, 0.32, terminating

13. $\frac{7}{10}$ 14. $\frac{13}{25}$ 15. $\frac{19}{20}$ 16. $\frac{11}{50}$ 17. $\frac{94}{99}$

18. $\frac{38}{9}$ 19. b   20. a   21. d   22. c

23. $0.\overline{1}, 0.\overline{2}, 0.\overline{3}, 0.\overline{4}, 0.\overline{5}, 0.\overline{6}$
    Each number is a repeating decimal. The digit which is repeating is increasing by one.

24. $\frac{14}{3}$ in., $4\frac{2}{3}$ in., $4.\overline{6}$ in.

25. $\frac{4}{1}$ in., 4 in., 4.0 in.

26. 0.2, 0.16, 0.12, 0.22, 0.1, 0.15, 0.05;
    Jose, Ken, Vicki, Doug, Cindy, Brenda, JiLynn

■ **Lesson 6.7**

1. $\frac{1}{16}$ 2. $-\frac{1}{27}$ 3. 1   4. 9

5. $\frac{3}{x^2}$ 6. $\frac{1}{16x^2}$ 7. $(-3)^{-2} = \frac{1}{9}$

8. $14^{-1} = \frac{1}{14}$ 9. x^5 10. $3^7 = 2187$

11. 8   12. x^3 13. 14539.336

14. 7396   15. 1024   16. 4   17. 0

18. -14 19. 7   20. 9   21. 3

22. $8^{-5} \cdot 8^7$ 23. $\frac{5^6}{5^{-4}}$ 24. >   25. >

26. >   27. 5^5 sq yd   28. $4081.47

■ **Lesson 6.8**

1. 3.5×10^3 2. 6.2×10^4

3. 3.75×10^{-4} 4. 2.05×10^{-2}

5. 6.2153×10^7 6. 1.05×10^{-5}

7. 320,000   8. 0.000635

9. 0.0043   10. 97,500   11. 0.00000827

12. 325,000   13. Yes

14. No, 3.5×10^5 15. No, 2.65×10^{-2}

16. Yes   17. No, 7.64×10^{-1}

18. Yes   19. 1.28×10^8; 128,000,000

20. 1.95×10^6; 1,950,000

21. 3.744×10^{-9}; 0.000000003744

22. 2.185×10^{-3}; 0.002185

23. $1 \times 10^6 > 6 \times 10^5$ because $1{,}000{,}000 > 600{,}000$.

24. $1 \times 10^{-4} < 4 \times 10^{-3}$ because $0.0001 < 0.004$.

25. Approximately 4.4688×10^{14} mi

26. 0.006, 6.0×10^{-3} gal; 1.994 gal

■ Lesson 6.9

1.

n	1	2	3	4	5	6
$n^2 - n$	0	2	6	12	20	30

2.

n	1	2	3	4	5	6
$n^2 + 2$	3	6	11	18	27	38

3. Possible answer: Add 1 to the denominator of the preceding fraction; $\frac{1}{5}, \frac{1}{6}, \frac{1}{7}$

4. Possible answer: The denominators increase by consecutive odd integers; $\frac{1}{37}, \frac{1}{50}, \frac{1}{65}$

5. Each term is the sum of the two previous terms plus one; 41, 67, 109

6. 9 and 11;

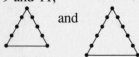 and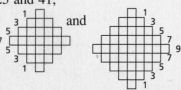

7. 25 and 41;

and

8. Possible answers: 11 and 29, 3 and 37

9. Possible answers: 11 and 19, 7 and 23

10. The midsegment of each side is replaced by 2 new segments.

11. 3 in star 1, 6 in star 2, 18 in star 3

12. The factors of 48 except for 1 and 48 are 2, 3, 4, 6, 8, 12, 16, and 24.

The factors of 75 except for 1 of 75 are 3, 5, 15, and 25.

$75 = 2 + 3 + 4 + 6 + 8 + 12 + 16 + 24$ and $48 = 3 + 5 + 15 + 25$

■ Lesson 7.1

1. $\frac{5}{7}$ 2. $\frac{1}{4}$ 3. $-\frac{1}{3}$ 4. $\frac{2}{5}$ 5. $-\frac{19}{3}$

6. $\frac{23}{3}$ 7. $\frac{3x}{4}$ 8. $-\frac{z}{7}$ 9. $-2c$

10. $-\frac{4}{x}$ 11. $\frac{6}{z}$ 12. $-\frac{19}{5k}$ 13. $-\frac{9}{4}$

14. 3   15. -1 16. -2 17. $-\frac{5}{3}$

18. -1 19. 0.67 20. -0.45 21. -0.88

22. $\frac{3}{6}, \frac{5}{6}, \frac{7}{6}$; every fraction after the first is $\frac{2}{6}$ greater than the preceding fraction. The next three numbers are $\frac{9}{6}, \frac{11}{6}, \frac{13}{6}$.

23. $\frac{11}{3}, -\frac{9}{3}, \frac{7}{3}$; the numerators are odd numbers decreasing in order with every other term being negative and the denominators are three. The next three numbers are $-\frac{5}{3}, \frac{3}{3}, -\frac{1}{3}$.

24. $\frac{3}{8} + \frac{4}{8} = \frac{7}{8}$ 25. $\frac{5}{6} - \frac{3}{6} = \frac{2}{6}$

26. 506 inches

27. a. $\$48\frac{4}{8} = \$48\frac{1}{2}$
    b. $\$50\frac{1}{8}$
    c. $\$48\frac{3}{8}$

■ Lesson 7.2

1. $\frac{3}{4}$ 2. $\frac{1}{14}$ 3. $-\frac{9}{16}$ 4. $\frac{17}{24}$ 5. $-\frac{13}{18}$

6. $\frac{1}{30}$ 7. $\frac{5x}{8}$ 8. $-\frac{7a}{12}$ 9. $\frac{15 + 6y}{5y}$

10. $-\frac{9}{14t}$ 11. $\frac{5b - 2a}{ab}$ 12. $\frac{21 + 2n}{3mn}$

13. -0.06 14. 0.71 15. 0.60

16. $\frac{307}{24} = 12\frac{19}{24}$ 17. $\frac{311}{24} = 12\frac{23}{24}$

18. $\frac{1}{8}$ 19. $\frac{1}{5}$

20. a. Hank;   b. $\frac{1}{6}$ c. $\frac{5}{12}$
    d. $\frac{1}{6} + \frac{3}{8} + \frac{5}{24} + \frac{1}{4} = \frac{4}{24} + \frac{9}{24} + \frac{5}{24} + \frac{6}{24}$
    $= \frac{24}{24} = 1$

■ Lesson 7.3

1. 0.96 2. 0.693 3. 9.05 4. -1.39

5. 7.877 6. 4.247 7. $\frac{5}{16} + \frac{2}{6} \approx 0.65$

8. $\frac{8}{16} + \frac{5}{9} \approx 1.06$ 9. Answers vary.

10. Answers vary.   11. Answers vary.

12. $\approx 0.676 - 0.626 \approx 0.05$

13. $\approx 0.806m + 0.457m \approx 1.26m$

14. $\approx 2 - (0.702 + 0.842 + 0.24) \approx 0.22$

15. $\approx 5x - (0.571x + 0.545x) \approx 3.88x$

16. $\approx 5.25 + 3.222 - 2.545 \approx 5.93$

17. $\approx 4x - (0.556x - 1.333x) \approx 4.78x$

18. $\frac{81}{100}$ or 0.81   **19.** $\frac{19}{100}$ or 0.19

20. $\frac{3}{4}$ or 0.75

21. a, to avoid a round-off error, you should begin by rounding the numbers to 3-decimal places—one place more than is required in the final result.

■ **Lesson 7.4**

1. $\frac{1}{9}$ **2.** $-\frac{9}{25}$ **3.** $-\frac{49}{68}$ **4.** $-\frac{91}{5}$

5. $\frac{33}{7}$ **6.** $-\frac{2}{15}$ **7.** $6x$ **8.** $56y$

9. $-\frac{1}{6}$ **10.** $-\frac{2}{5}$ **11.** $\frac{3z}{5}$ **12.** $-16x$

13. $\frac{15}{4}$ sq in.   **14.** $\frac{153}{8}$ sq in.

15. $\frac{21}{2}$ sq in.   **16.** 0.545   **17.** 3.167

18. -5.438 **19.** $\frac{27}{100}$ **20.** $\frac{3}{20}$ **21.** $\frac{9}{40}$

22. $\frac{62}{3}$ hr $= 20\frac{2}{3}$ hr   **23.** \$30,600

■ **Lesson 7.5**

1. $\frac{5}{1}$ **2.** $\frac{y}{7}$ **3.** $\frac{4}{3z}$

4. $-\frac{4}{29}$ **5.** $\frac{1}{16x}$ **6.** $-8m$

7. Did not multiply by the reciprocal.

$$10 \div 3\frac{1}{5} = 10 \div \frac{16}{5}$$
$$= 10 \cdot \frac{5}{16}$$
$$= \frac{10 \cdot 5}{16}$$
$$= \frac{25}{8}$$

8. Did not multiply by the reciprocal.

$$\frac{2}{3} \div \frac{1}{6} = \frac{2}{3} \cdot \frac{6}{1}$$
$$= \frac{2 \cdot 6}{3 \cdot 1}$$
$$= 4$$

9. $\frac{3}{16}$ **10.** $\frac{1}{8}$ **11.** $\frac{3}{32}$ **12.** $\frac{5}{12}$ **13.** $\frac{5}{18}$

14. $\frac{5}{24}$ **15.** $\frac{3}{4}$ **16.** $\frac{9}{8}$ **17.** $\frac{3}{2}$ **18.** $\frac{5}{3}$

19. $\frac{5}{2}$ **20.** $\frac{10}{3}$ **21.** $\frac{6}{5}$ **22.** $-\frac{72}{7}$ **23.** $-\frac{7}{4}$

24. $\frac{64}{189}$ **25.** $\frac{19}{5z}$ **26.** $\frac{7p}{23}$ **27.** 40 loads

28. $\frac{69}{8}$ ounces $\left(8\frac{5}{8}\right)$; $\frac{23}{8}$ ounces $\left(2\frac{7}{8}\right)$

■ **Lesson 7.6**

1. 36%   **2.** 70%   **3.** 40%   **4.** 50%

5. The least is d, 25%. The greatest is a, 75%.

6. 10%   **7.** 48%   **8.** 40%

9. 65%   **10.** 60%   **11.** 49%

12. Answers vary.   **13.** Answers vary.

14. Answers vary.   **15.** \$1500

16.

Area	Percent
House payment	34%
Food	28%
Car payment	10%
Electricity	4%
Water	6%
Heat	2%
Phone	1%
Entertainment	5%
Clothing	10%

17. c, because the shaded region is 50% of the entire area. The other three figures all have 75% of the area shaded.

■ **Lesson 7.7**

1. 0.48   **2.** 0.16   **3.** 2.50   **4.** 0.842

5. 0.005   **6.** 0.384   **7.** 63%   **8.** 92%

9. 165%   **10.** 0.8%   **11.** 2.1%   **12.** 38.4%

13. $=$ **14.** $<$ **15.** $>$ **16.** $>$ **17.** $\frac{17}{25}$

18. $\frac{7}{20}$ **19.** $\frac{79}{100}$ **20.** $\frac{5}{4}$ **21.** $\frac{69}{20}$ **22.** $\frac{21}{20}$

23. 87.5%   **24.** 65%   **25.** 40%

26. 375%   **27.** 22%   **28.** 225%

29. $55.\overline{5}\%$ **30.** $58.\overline{3}\%$ **31.** 31.25%

32.

Reason	Percent	Decimal	Fraction
Bored	36%	0.36	$\frac{9}{25}$
Moving	19%	0.19	$\frac{19}{100}$
New Furniture	15%	0.15	$\frac{3}{20}$
Redecorating	16%	0.16	$\frac{4}{25}$
Other	14%	0.14	$\frac{7}{50}$

33.

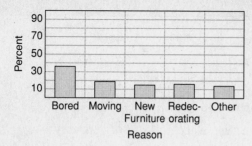

■ Lesson 7.8

1. 0.18, 144　　**2.** 0.23, 27.6　　**3.** 3.6, 28.8

4. 1.75, 70　　**5.** 0.006, 3.24　　**6.** 0.035, 5.25

7. c, 4　　**8.** d, 30　　**9.** a, 13.$\overline{3}$　　**10.** b, 6.$\overline{6}$

11. 5 squares　　　　　　**12.** 15 squares

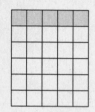　　　　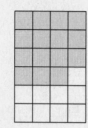

13. 40.7　　**14.** 7.02　　**15.** 197.88

16. 273.6　　**17.** 21.05　　**18.** 254.52

19. Perimeter = 48 cm, area = 135 sq cm

20. Perimeter = 16 cm, area = 15 sq cm

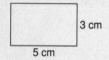

3 cm

5 cm

21. Perimeter = 16 cm.
Yes, it is a linear measure.

22. Area = 45 cm². No, because $33\frac{1}{3}\%$ of 135 $\neq$ ($33\frac{1}{3}\%$ of 15) $\times$ ($33\frac{1}{3}\%$ of 9). You can see that the percentage rate is multiplied twice on the right and only once on the left.

23. $63.96　　**24.** ≈ $657.44

■ Lesson 7.9

1. $8.43　　**2.** $62.91　　**3.** $144.15

4. 0.2%　　**5.** 12.2%　　**6.** 4.6%　　**7.** 3.8%

8. 0.3%　　**9.** 7.2%　　**10.** 4.4%　　**11.** 4.8%

12. 1.4%　　**13.** 6.9%　　**14.** 2.5%　　**15.** 0.2%

16. Amount of raise = $1206.80
New salary = $18,446.80

17. 78,540 seats　　**18.** 980 freshmen

19. Increase: $2056.50
Current Price: $22,621.50

20. ≈ 19.6% laid off, ≈ 80.4% retained
Yes, 80.4% of 153 ≈ 123 people, which is the number of employees retained

21. ≈ 71.7% in December
≈ 28.3% in other months

■ Lesson 8.1

1. A rate, 8 feet per second

2. A ratio, $\frac{19}{36}$ or 19 to 36

3. A rate, ≈ 1.27 hits per game $\left(\dfrac{14 \text{ hits}}{11 \text{ game}}\right)$

4. $\dfrac{3 \text{ miles}}{24 \text{ minutes}} = \dfrac{1 \text{ miles}}{8 \text{ minute}} = 0.125$ miles per minute; a rate because different units of measure

5. $\dfrac{10 \text{ students}}{60 \text{ students}} = \dfrac{1}{6}$ or 1 to 6; a ratio because same units of measure

6. $\dfrac{2 \text{ inches}}{40 \text{ minutes}} = \dfrac{1 \text{ inches}}{20 \text{ minutes}} = 0.05$ inch per minute; a rate because different units of measure

7. $\dfrac{2 \text{ pictures}}{3 \text{ pictures}} = \dfrac{2}{3}$ or 2 to 3; a ratio because same units of measure

8. $\dfrac{144 \text{ in.}}{16 \text{ in.}} = 9$ to 1　　**9.** $\dfrac{32000 \text{ m}}{4000 \text{ m}} = 8$ to 1

10. $\dfrac{36 \text{ hr}}{168 \text{ hr}} = 3$ to 14　　**11.** $\dfrac{7 \text{ pt}}{16 \text{ pt}} = 7$ to 16

12. $\dfrac{36 \text{ in.}}{28 \text{ in.}} = 9$ to 7　　**13.** $\dfrac{32 \text{ oz}}{24 \text{ oz}} = 4$ to 3

14. 50 cubic feet per hour

15. a. 24.25 miles per gallon

b. ≈ 59.7 miles per hour

16. b. one gallon for $4.25 is the better bargain because you pay about $1.06 per quart whereas the other is about $1.08 per quart.

17. a. the 36-ounce box for $3.72 is the better bargain because you pay about $0.10 per ounce, whereas, the other is about $0.11 per ounce.

18. Ratio of the perimeters is $\frac{14}{24} = 7$ to 12.
Ratio of the areas is $\frac{12}{24} = 1$ to 2.

19. Ratio of the perimeters is $\frac{36}{24} = 3$ to 2.
Ratio of the areas is $\frac{72}{24} = 3$ to 1.

■ Lesson 8.2

1. Yes, $1 \cdot 42 = 6 \cdot 7$ **2.** No, $2 \cdot 9 \neq 3 \cdot 4$

3. No, $5 \cdot 120 \neq 12 \cdot 10$ **4.** 3

5. 12   **6.** 80   **7.** 36   **8.** 7   **9.** 6

10. $\dfrac{x}{5} = \dfrac{12}{15}, x = 4$ **11.** $\dfrac{y}{12} = \dfrac{2}{3}, y = 8$

12. $\dfrac{4}{9} = \dfrac{24}{z}, z = 54$ **13.** $\dfrac{7}{11} = \dfrac{y}{99}, y = 63$

14. $\dfrac{3}{4} = \dfrac{w}{18}, w = \dfrac{27}{2}$ **15.** $\dfrac{t}{10} = \dfrac{3}{35}, t = \dfrac{6}{7}$

16. 30.33   **17.** 3.2   **18.** 14.06

19. $d = 24, e = 18$ **20.** $q = 13, r = 5$

21. 5 bags   **22.** 300 cement blocks

23. 2000 defective parts

■ Lesson 8.3

1. 105 teachers

2. a. 56 kph

   b. Yes, you are traveling 68.75 mph.

3. $18\frac{3}{4}$ cups of flour   **4.** 85 inches of snow

5. 110 employees   **6.** 22 days

7. $93\frac{3}{4}$ pounds   **8.** $46\frac{2}{3}$ minutes

9. $\approx$ 21,691 people

■ Lesson 8.4

1. 3.2%   **2.** 86.4   **3.** 39.56   **4.** 650

5. 21.6   **6.** 1368   **7.** 1569.5   **8.** 14

9. 106.98%   **10.** 45   **11.** 100   **12.** 300

13. 10%   **14.** 150

15. $\dfrac{25}{675} = \dfrac{p}{100}, p = 3.70\%$

16. $\dfrac{a}{162} = \dfrac{52}{100}, a = 84.24$

17. $p = 25\%$ **18.** $a = 20$

Possible model: Possible model:

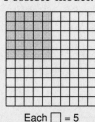

Each ☐ = 5

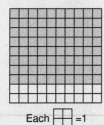

Each ⊞ =1

19. $b = 80$ Possible model:

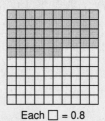

Each ☐ = 0.8

20. \$975.48

21. Sales tax = \$87, total bill = \$1537

22. \$3.05 is the tip. $\approx$ 18.0% tip rate (17.99%)

23. $\approx$ \$35,714.29

■ Lesson 8.5

1. \$12,500   **2.** \$3375   **3.** \$1125

4. \$1500   **5.** 5.727×10^7 sq mi

6. 1.168×10^7 sq mi   **7.** 5.097×10^6 sq mi

8. 1.718×10^7 sq mi   **9.** 2.978×10^6 sq mi

10. 9.335×10^6 sq mi   **11.** 5.097×10^6 sq mi

12.

Country	Percent	Population
China	21%	1.151×10^9
India	16%	8.768×10^8
former Soviet Union	5%	2.74×10^8
United States	5%	2.74×10^8
Indonesia	4%	2.192×10^8
Brazil	3%	1.644×10^8

13. \$21,116.67

14. They played 40 games and won 38.

15. \$17.31

■ Lesson 8.6

1. A 25% increase   **2.** A $33\frac{1}{3}\%$ decrease

3. A 20% decrease   **4.** A $16\frac{2}{3}\%$ increase

5. A 25% decrease   **6.** A 5% increase

7. $\approx$ a 1.7% increase   **8.** $\approx$ a 7.7% decrease

9. $\approx$ a 12.7% increase   **10.** $\approx$ a 2.2% decrease

11. Each number is a 300% increase of the preceding number. 512, 2048, 8192

12. Each number is a 50% decrease of the preceding number. 40, 20, 10

13. Each number is a 900% increase of the preceding number. 10,000, 100,000, 1,000,000

14. Each number is a 60% decrease of the preceding number. 400, 160, 64

15. False, four times a number is a 300% increase of the number

16. True

17. False, a 90% decrease of 60 is $60 - 54 = 6$.

18. True   **19.** Answers vary.

20. Answers vary.

21.

Original Number	New Number	Percent Change
55	66	20% increase
55	44	20% decrease
200	350	75% increase
1400	350	75% decrease
60	75	25% increase
60	45	25% decrease

22. A $66\frac{2}{3}$% decrease   **23.** $\approx$ a 7.0% increase

■ **Lesson 8.7**

1. 720 ways

2. 15 gifts

white shirt-dark blue tie	1
white shirt-stripe blue tie	2
white shirt-paisley tie	3
white w/blue stripe shirt-dark blue tie	4
white w/blue stripe shirt-stripe blue tie	5
white w/blue stripe shirt-paisley tie	6
off white shirt-dark blue tie	7
off white shirt-stripe blue tie	8
off white shirt-paisley tie	9
light blue shirt-dark blue tie	10
light blue shirt-stripe blue tie	11
light blue shirt-paisley tie	12
light blue w/stripe shirt-dark blue tie	13
light blue w/stripe shirt-stripe blue tie	14
light blue w/stripe shirt-paisley tie	15

3.

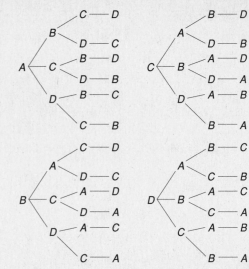

24 ways; the probability that Angel and Bo will be standing next to each other is $\frac{12}{24} = \frac{1}{2}$.

4. 125,000 combinations; $\dfrac{1}{125,000}$

5. 35,152 combinations of call letters
The probability that second letter is a Q is $\dfrac{1352}{35152} = \dfrac{1}{26}$.

6. 180 times

■ **Lesson 8.8**

1. 36 outcomes possible

2.

3. Two is the smallest and 12 is the largest.

4. **a.** $\frac{1}{36}$ **d.** $\frac{18}{36} = \frac{1}{2}$

    b. $\frac{12}{36} = \frac{1}{3}$ **e.** $\frac{35}{36}$

    c. $\frac{6}{36} = \frac{1}{6}$ **f.** $\frac{21}{36} = \frac{7}{12}$

5. Answers vary. Experimental probabilities should approach theoretical probabilities as the number of trials increase.

6. 64 ways   7. $\frac{1}{64}$ 8. $\frac{1}{16}$

9. 720 ways   10. $\frac{1}{720}$ 11. $\frac{1}{120}$

■ **Lesson 9.1**

1. $6, -6$ 2. $\sqrt{12}, -\sqrt{12}$ 3. $1.4, -1.4$

4. $0.8, -0.8$ 5. $20, -20$ 6. $\frac{5}{6}, -\frac{5}{6}$

7.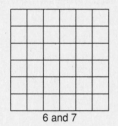

8.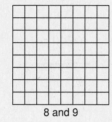

     6 and 7   8 and 9

9.

     5 and 6

10. $5, -5$ 11. $25, -25$ 12. $5.477, -5.477$

13. $5.196, -5.196$ 14. $8, -8$ 15. $4, -4$

In Exercises 16–18., estimates may vary slightly.

16. $5.5, \sqrt{30} \approx 5.477$ 17. $6.8, \sqrt{45} \approx 6.708$

18. $3.1, \sqrt{10} \approx 3.162$ 19. $x = \sqrt{121}, x = 11$

20. $q^2 - 10 = 39, q = 7, -7$

21. $25y^2 = 49, y = \frac{7}{5}, -\frac{7}{5}$

22. 12 ft by 12 ft   23. 26 sq ft

24. ≈ 5.1 ft by 5.1 ft   25. ≈ 20.4 ft

■ **Lesson 9.2**

1. Rational, a quotient of integers

2. Rational, a quotient of integers

3. Irrational, cannot be written as a quotient of integers (or decimal is non-terminating, non-repeating)

4. Rational, $-\sqrt{16} = -4$, an integer is always a rational number

5. Irrational, cannot be written as a quotient of integers (or decimal is non-terminating, non-repeating)

6. Rational, $\sqrt{\frac{9}{4}} = \frac{3}{2}$, a quotient of integers

7. Sometimes, for example $\frac{3}{2}$ is rational but not an integer.

8. Sometimes, for example $\sqrt{2}$ is irrational but $\sqrt{4}$ is rational.

9. Never, integers are always rational.

10. Always, real numbers are rational and irrational.

11. $\sqrt{18}$, irrational, cannot be written as quotient of integers (or non-terminating, non-repeating decimal)

12. -3, rational, result is an integer

13. $\dfrac{\sqrt{2}}{6}$, irrational, not a quotient of integers

14. c   15. b   16. a   17. e   18. d

19–23.

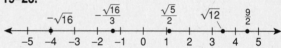

24. $>$ 25. $<$ 26. $>$ 27. $<$ 28. $>$

29. $<$ 30. $\sqrt{32}$ 31. $\sqrt{50}$ 32. $\sqrt{4.5}$ or $\sqrt{\frac{9}{2}}$

■ **Lesson 9.3**

1. $c = 10$ 2. $b = 36$ 3. $a = 40$

4. $b = 40$ 5. $a = 7$ 6. $c = 53$

7. $c = 35$ 8. $b = 30$ 9. $a = 18$

10.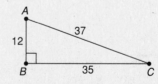

11. Not a right triangle

12.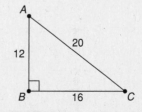

13.

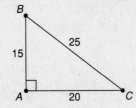

14. Not a right triangle

15.

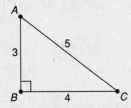

16. Not a right triangle

17.

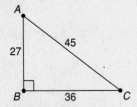

18. $b = 52$ **19.** $a = 48$ **20.** $b = 60$

21. The maximum height the ladder will reach is about 38.7 feet, and the minimum height is about 35.7 feet.

22. About 130.3 feet ($127.3 + 3$)

23. About 17 miles

24. About 179 feet (178.9)

■ **Lesson 9.4**

1. $P = 82$ units, $A = 420$ sq units

2. $P = 20$ units, $A = 25$ sq units

3. $P = 108$ units, $A = 306$ sq units

4. 6 feet from the base

5. ≈ 180.3 miles   **6.** ≈ 43.0 yards

7. ≈ 204.9 feet ($60 + 60 + 84.9$)

■ **Lesson 9.5**

1.

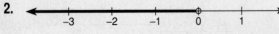

2.

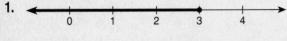

3.

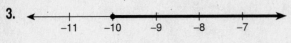

4.

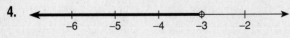

5.

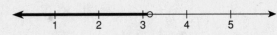

6.

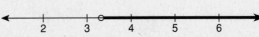

7. $x > -2$ **8.** $x \le 15$ **9.** $x < 0$

10. $x \ge 0$ **11.** $x \le 3$ **12.** $x > -5$

13. $x < \sqrt{10}$

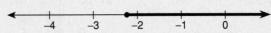

14. $x > \sqrt{11}$

15. $x \ge -\sqrt{5}$

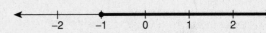

16. $x \le -\sqrt{15}$

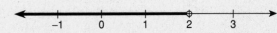

17. $w \ge -1$

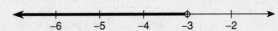

18. $x < 2$

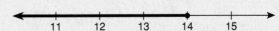

19. $y < -3$

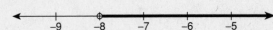

20. $r \le 14$

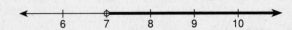

21. $-8 < t$

22. $7 < x$

23. $5 \le x$, 5 is less than or equal to x.

24. $-10 \ge t$, -10 is greater than or equal to t.

25. $-4 < w$, -4 is less than w.

26. $q + 12 < -4$, $q < -16$

27. $z - 10 \le 5$, $z \le 15$

28. $p - 16 > -12$, $p > 4$

29. $42 \ge t + 22$, $20 \ge t$ **30.** $a \ge 13$

31. $h > 18$ **32.** $t \le -5$ **33.** $h > 2$

34. Answers vary. **35.** Answers vary.

■ Lesson 9.6

1. The direction of the inequality symbol is not reversed when you multiply both sides by a positive number. Line 2 should be

$$\frac{1}{5} \cdot 5x \le \frac{1}{5} \cdot (-32)$$
$$x \le -\frac{32}{5}.$$

2. The direction of the inequality symbol is reversed when you multiply both sides by a negative number. Line 2 should be

$$-2 \cdot \left(-\frac{1}{2}\right)z < -2 \cdot (-5)$$
$$z < 10.$$

3. c **4.** b **5.** a **6.** d

7. $n < \frac{12}{5}$

8. $m > -\frac{11}{3}$

9. $x \ge 24$

10. $\frac{5}{3} \ge k$

11. $-\frac{3}{32} > c$

12. $-\frac{3}{5} \le w$

13. $p \ge -25$

14. $-\frac{19}{6} \le m$

15. $37.5 < p$

16. $a < -72$

17. $d < -\frac{3}{2}$

18. $w > -0.4$

19. At least 345 pounds

20. At least $56.\overline{6}$ mph

21. $15.00 per square yard

22. 20 singles

■ Lesson 9.7

1. The direction of the inequality symbol is reversed when you divide both sides by a negative number. Line 3 should be

$$\frac{-3x}{-3} \ge \frac{7}{-3}$$
$$x \ge -\frac{7}{3}.$$

2. The direction of the inequality symbol is not reversed when you add a negative number to both sides. Line 3 should be

$$15y + 10 - 10 > -3 - 10$$
$$15y > -13$$
$$y > -\frac{13}{15}.$$

3. Never **4.** Always

5. b **6.** a **7.** c **8.** d

9. $x < -3$ **10.** $z \ge -180$ **11.** $a < 3$

12. $x \le 40$ **13.** $x \ge 5$ **14.** $x > -\frac{19}{2}$

15. $2n + 2n + 2 + 2n + 4 \le 18;\ n \le 2$

16. $2n + 2n + 2 + 2n + 4 > 66;\ n > 10$

17. $2n + 2n + 2 + 2n + 4 < -12;\ n < -3$

18. $x \le 12$ **19.** $x > 5$

20. You must earn at least a 92 on the sixth exam.

■ Lesson 9.8

1. No, $2 + 5 \not> 8$ **2.** Yes

3. No, $8 + 10 \not> 18$ **4.** Yes

5.

Measure of Side 3 is greater than	Measure of Side 3 is less than
6 in.	14 in.
8 cm	26 cm
8 ft	32 ft
30 m	120 m
45 yd	295 yd

6. Yes **7.** Yes **8.** Yes **9.** Yes

10. No **11.** No **12.** $e + d$

13. b **14.** a **15.** d

16. 2 in., 6 in., 6 in.; 3 in., 5 in., 6 in.: 4 in., 4 in., 6 in.; 4 in., 5 in., 5 in.

17. a. Yes, a triangle can be formed by side lengths of three consecutive integers except for the case of lengths 1, 2, 3.
 b. Yes, a triangle can be formed by side lengths of three consecutive even integers except for the case of lengths 2, 4, 6.
 c. Yes, a triangle can be formed by side lengths of three consecutive odd integers except for the case of lengths 1, 3, 5.

18. 35 ft < 3rd side < 585 ft; at least 1170 feet; less than 550 feet

■ **Lesson 10.1**

1. $\overline{OP}, \overline{PU}, \overline{OU}$

2. $\overrightarrow{PO}, \overrightarrow{PQ}, \overrightarrow{PR}, \overrightarrow{PN}, \overrightarrow{PU}$

3. $\overleftrightarrow{NR}$ and $\overleftrightarrow{OU}$, $\overleftrightarrow{MS}$ and $\overleftrightarrow{OU}$

4. $\overleftrightarrow{NR}$ and $\overleftrightarrow{MS}$ **5.** $\overrightarrow{OP}, \overrightarrow{PU}$, or $\overrightarrow{OU}$

6. $\overline{RP}$ **7.** a ray **8.** a line

9. The length of a line segment

10. a line segment **11.** 7

12. A, B, C, D, E or F, G, H, I, J

13. $\overleftrightarrow{DE}, \overleftrightarrow{GH}, \overleftrightarrow{FJ}$ **14.** $\overrightarrow{IC}, \overrightarrow{IH}, \overrightarrow{IJ}$

15. 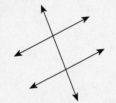 **16.**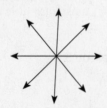

17. Yes **18.** Yes **19.** planes

■ **Lesson 10.2**

1. ∠ZVW or ∠YVW, ∠ZYW, ∠ZYX, ∠WYX, ∠YWX, ∠VWZ, ∠YWZ

2. ∠VWY, ∠XWZ

3. ∠WZV, ∠WZY, ∠YXW

4. ∠VWZ, ∠YWZ, ∠XWY, ∠VWY, ∠XWZ, ∠XWV

5. c **6.** a **7.** d **8.** b

9. 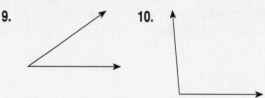 **10.**

11. 80° **12.** 130°

13. 80° acute angle **14.** 142.5°, obtuse angle

15. c **16.** a **17.** b

■ **Lesson 10.3**

1. $m \parallel n$

2. No, l and p are not parallel, so their corresponding angles are not congruent.

3. ∠12, ∠10 **4.** ∠2, ∠4, ∠8, ∠6

5. ∠1 and ∠5, ∠4 and ∠8, ∠2 and ∠6, ∠3 and ∠7

6. ∠1 ≅ ∠2 Corresponding angles of ∥ lines ≅ or
 ∠1 ≅ ∠6 corresponding angles of ∥ lines ≅
 ∠2 ≅ ∠3 Vertical angles ≅ or
 ∠2 ≅ ∠5 Corresponding angles of ∥ lines ≅
 ∠3 ≅ ∠4 Corresponding angles of ∥ lines ≅
 ∠4 ≅ ∠5 Vertical angles ≅
 ∠5 ≅ ∠6 Corresponding angles of ∥ lines ≅

7.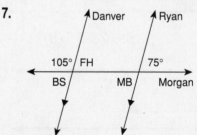

8. Accept all reasonable answers. Consider Morgan Road at the intersection with Danver Drive to be a straight angle. Therefore, the angle at which the fire hydrant is placed has a measure of 75°, 180° − 105° = 75°. Since this angle and the angle given at Ryan Street and Morgan Road are congruent, it can be shown that Danver Drive and Ryan Street are parallel. (Actually, we will prove formally later in the text.)

9. The fire hydrant, bus stop, and mailbox are all placed at 75° angles.

10.

■ **Lesson 10.4**

1. A vertical line of symmetry

2. A rotational symmetry of 180°, and 2 lines of symmetry

3. A horizontal line, a vertical line of symmetry, a rotational symmetry of 180°

4. 90° or 180° in either direction

5. 60°, 120°, or 180° in either direction

6. 45°, 90°, 135° or 180° in either direction

7. Answers may vary.   **8.** Answers may vary.

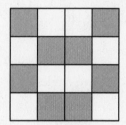

9. a. Answers vary.   **b.** Answers vary.

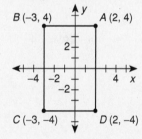

10. a. Answers vary.   **b.** Answers vary.

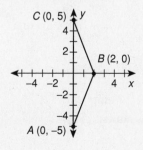

■ **Lesson 10.5**

In Exercises 1–3, sketches may vary slightly.

1. 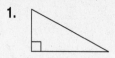   **2.**

3.   **4.** Acute isosceles

5. Right scalene   **6.** Right isosceles

In Exercises 7–8, sketches may vary slightly.

7. Right isosceles   **8.** Acute scalene

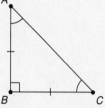
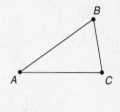

9. Perimeter $= 8 + 4\sqrt{2}$ units ≈ 13.66 units
Area $= 8$ square units

10. Perimeter $= 4 + 4\sqrt{2}$ units ≈ 9.66 units
Area $= 4$ square units

11. Perimeter $= 6 + 3\sqrt{2}$ units ≈ 10.24 units
Area $= \frac{9}{2}$ square units

12. Acute isosceles   **13.** Right scalene

14. Equilateral, equiangular   **15.** Sometimes

16. Never   **17.** Never   **18.** Sometimes

■ **Lesson 10.6**

1. Parallelogram   **2.** Rhombus

3. Trapezoid

4. Sometimes, A rectangle with 4 equal sides is a square.

5. Never, A parallelogram has opposite sides parallel, a trapezoid only has one pair of opposite sides parallel.

6. $x = 8$ cm, $y = 14$ cm

7. $x = y = 16$ yd   **8.** Not possible

9. Check students' sketches.
Accept all parallelograms.

10. $m\angle A = 110°$, isosceles trapezoid

11. $m\angle A = 65°$, parallelogram

12. $m\angle A = 90°$, kite

■ Lesson 10.7

1. b   **2.** a   **3.** c

4. equilateral: a, c; equiangular: a, b; regular: a

5. equilateral   **6.** equiangular

7. equilateral, equiangular, regular

In Exercises 8–10, sketches may vary slightly.

8.   **9.**

10.

11. $x = 3$

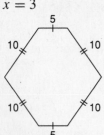

12. $x = 4$

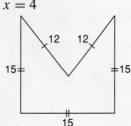

13. $x = 4$

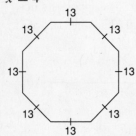

■ Lesson 10.8

1. 40°   **2.** 90°   **3.** 110°   **4.** 5   **5.** 9

6. 12   **7.** 9   **8.** 6   **9.** 3   **10.** 144°, 36°

11. 120°, 60°   **12.** 160°, 20°   **13.** 8   **14.** 10

15. 68°, 88°, 108°, 128°, 148°

16. 82.5°, 97.5°, 112.5°, 127.5°, 142.5°, 157.5°

■ Lesson 10.9

1. $\overline{MK}$ shortest, $\overline{LK}$ longest

2. $\overline{AB}$ shortest, $\overline{AC}$ longest

3. $\overline{XZ}$ shortest, $\overline{ZY}$ longest

4. $\angle C$ smallest, $m\angle A = m\angle B$ largest

5. $\angle G$ smallest, $\angle F$ largest

6. $\angle H$ smallest, $\angle I$ largest

7. $\overline{AC}, \overline{AB}, \overline{BC}, \overline{DC}, \overline{BD}$

8. $\overline{KM}, \overline{KL}, \overline{LM}, \overline{LN}, \overline{NM}$

9. $x = 15$, $\angle B$ smallest, $\angle A$ largest, $\overline{AC}$ smallest, $\overline{BC}$ longest

10. $x = 10$, $\angle F$ smallest, $\angle FED$ largest, $\overline{DE}$ smallest, $\overline{DF}$ largest

11. b.; An equilateral triangle is also equiangular.

12. c.; An isosceles triangle has two angles of equal measure.

13. a.; Length of the sides satisfies the Pythagorean theorem.

14.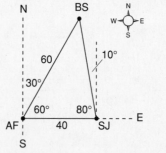

$m\angle AF = 60°$

$m\angle SJ = 80°$

$m\angle BS = 40°$

Therefore, Angel Falls and Buck Springs are furthest apart. Angel Falls and San José are closest. The distance between Buck Springs and San José $40 < d < 60$.

■ Lesson 11.1

1. 108 units², $3(108) = 324$ units² or $\frac{1}{2}(12 + 24) \cdot 18 = 324$ units²

2. $25\sqrt{3}$ units^2, $2(25\sqrt{3}) = 50\sqrt{3}$ units^2 or $(10)(5\sqrt{3}) = 50\sqrt{3}$ units^2

3. $4 \times$ Area of triangle = Area of hexagon, $4(36\sqrt{3}) = 144\sqrt{3}$ units^2; $P = 36$ units; $P = 72$ units

4. $6 \times$ Area of triangle = Area of hexagon, $6(4\sqrt{3}) = 24\sqrt{3}$ units^2; $P = 12$ units; $P = 24$ units

In Exercises 5 and 6, one possible answer is given.

5.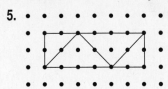

12 units^2
16 units

6.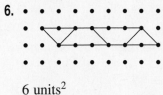

6 units^2
$12 + 2\sqrt{2}$ units

7. 1800 ft^2 **8.** 8712 ft^2 **9.** 106 units^2

■ **Lesson 11.2**

1. $\angle X$ **2.** $\overline{YZ}$ **3.** $\angle Z$ **4.** $\overline{BC}$
5. $\angle B$ **6.** $\overline{AC}$ **7.** $\overline{DF}$
8. $\angle N$ **9.** $m\angle X$ **10.** NO
11. a and d; b and c   **12.** c and d

13–15. Answers vary. One possible answer given.

13. 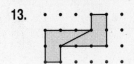   **14.**

15. 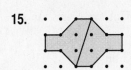   **16.**

17. 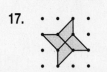   **18.**

19. 16   **20.** 9

■ **Lesson 11.3**

1. $X' = (-3, -4)$, $Y' = (-1, -2)$, $Z' = (-4, -1)$

2. $X' = (3, 4)$, $Y' = (1, 2)$, $Z' = (4, 1)$

3. $X' = (3, -4)$, $Y' = (1, -2)$, $Z' = (4, -1)$

4. $X' = (3, -4)$, $Y' = (1, -2)$, $Z' = (4, -1)$

5. $X' = (-3, 4)$, $Y' = (-1, 2)$, $Z' = (-4, 1)$

6.   **7.**

8.

9. Yes   **10.** No   **11.** No

12. 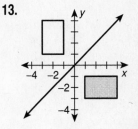   **13.**

14.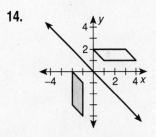

15. A, H, I, M, O, T, U, V, W, X, Y

16. "OH MOM MY MOUTH TOO HOT"

17. Answers vary.

■ **Lesson 11.4**

1. 90°   **2.** 180°   **3.** 90°
4. 80° clockwise   **5.** 120° counterclockwise
6. 35° counterclockwise
7. $\overline{DE}$ **8.** $\overline{KF}$ **9.** $\overline{PK}$
10. $\overline{OQ}$ **11.** $\triangle HAB$ **12.** $QLMO$

13.

14.

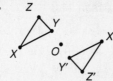

15.

Lesson 11.5

1. b.; 5 units left and 6 units up.

2. c.; 3 units left and 5 units down.

3. a.; 5 units left and 4 units down.

4. c   5. a   6. b

7.

8.

9.

10. ANGEL   11. Answers vary

Lesson 11.6

1. a and c   2. a and c   3. a and b

4. Yes, $\frac{5}{4}$ 5. No

6. $\frac{AB}{JK} = \frac{BC}{KL} = \frac{CD}{LM} = \frac{DA}{MJ}$ (or reciprocals)

7. $\frac{2}{1}$ 8. a. 16, b. 17, c. 13

9. L 10. $\frac{3}{1}, \frac{20}{3}$ 11. $\frac{4}{1}, \frac{3}{2}$ 12. $\frac{3}{2}, 2$

Lesson 11.7

1. 5.8 ft high, 5.5 ft wide, 12.8 ft long

2. ≈ 80 ft   3. ≈ 616 m   4. ≈ 19,360 m²

5. ≈ 4.8 acres   6. ≈ 278 miles

7. $1\frac{1}{3}$ yd wide by 3 yd long

8. $346\frac{2}{3}$ yd, $8\frac{2}{3}$ yd   9. 40 times longer

10. $1\frac{1}{3}$ in. by 3 in.   11. Yes

12. 7 ft 6 in.

Lesson 11.8

1. $\frac{22}{\sqrt{548}} \approx 0.940$ 2. $\frac{8}{\sqrt{548}} \approx 0.342$

3. $\frac{8}{\sqrt{548}} \approx 0.342$ 4. $\frac{22}{\sqrt{548}} \approx 0.940$

5. $\frac{11}{4} = 2.75$ 6. $\frac{4}{11} = 0.\overline{36}$

7. $m\angle J = 53.3°$; $JL = \sqrt{101}$

$$\sin J = \frac{\sqrt{65}}{\sqrt{101}} \approx 0.802$$

$$\cos J = \frac{6}{\sqrt{101}} \approx 0.597$$

$$\tan J = \frac{\sqrt{65}}{6} \approx 1.34$$

$$\sin L = \frac{6}{\sqrt{101}} \approx 0.597$$

$$\cos L = \frac{\sqrt{65}}{\sqrt{101}} \approx 0.802$$

$$\tan L = \frac{6}{\sqrt{65}} \approx 0.744$$

8. $m\angle B = 28.1°$; $BC = 15$

$\sin A = \frac{15}{17}$ $\sin B = \frac{8}{17}$

$\cos A = \frac{8}{17}$ $\cos B = \frac{15}{17}$

$\tan A = \frac{15}{8}$ $\tan B = \frac{8}{15}$

9.

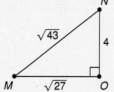

10.

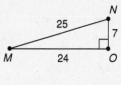

11.

x	80°	40°	20°	10°	5°	1°
$\sin x$	0.985	0.643	0.342	0.174	0.087	0.017
$\tan x$	5.671	0.839	0.364	0.176	0.087	0.017

12. As x gets smaller the values of $\sin x$ and $\tan x$ get closer.

13. As x gets smaller, the hypotenuse and the adjacent side become closer to the same length. Therefore, the ratios become closer.

14. and 15.

Length of guy wire (ft)	50	100	150	200
Vertical distance to guy wire (ft)	25	50	75	100
sine ratio	$\frac{25}{50}$	$\frac{50}{100}$	$\frac{75}{100}$	$\frac{100}{200}$

16. The sine ratio of opposite side to the hypotenuse remains constant.

■ Lesson 11.9

1. 1.8807   **2.** 0.5446   **3.** 0.9998

4. 15.49   **5.** 9.54   **6.** 5.71

7. $m\angle N = 48°$
$o = 20.07$
$n = 22.29$

8. $m\angle R = 61°$
$p = 6.65$
$q = 13.72$

9. $m\angle V = 28°$
$t = 15.05$
$s = 17.04$

10. ≈ 2145 ft

11. ≈ 184 ft   **12.** ≈ 499 ft

■ Lesson 12.1

1. 38.3 in., 116.8 in.^{2} **2.** 6.9 in., 3.8 in.^{2}

3. 8.8 ft, 6.2 ft^2 **4.** 89.2 in. 633.1 in.^{2}

5. 15.3 in., 30.6 in.   **6.** 9.2 cm, 18.4 cm

7. 29.4 cm^2 **8.** 28.5 in.^{2}

9. 518.1 ft   **10.** 85,486.5 ft^2

11. Middle radius = 6 in.,
Outer radius = 10 in.

12. Yellow area $\approx$ 12.6 in.^{2},
red area $\approx$ 100.5 in.^{2},
blue area $\approx$ 201 in.^{2}

■ Lesson 12.2

1. Prism   **2.** Cylinder   **3.** Cone

4.   **5.**

6.   **7.**

8.   **9.**

10. a. 8 faces, **b.** 12 vertices, **c.** 18 edges
11. a. 5 faces, **b.** 6 vertices, **c.** 9 edges
12. a. 10 faces, **b.** 16 vertices, **c.** 24 edges

■ Lesson 12.3

1. 401.9 cm^2 **2.** 88.0 in.^{2} **3.** 33.5 in.^{2}

4. 251.2 cm^2 **5.** 156 m^2 **6.** 178 ft^2

7. 263.8 m^2 **8.** 54 in.^{2} **9.** 126 in.^{2}

10. No, where the faces meet, the surface area has been eliminated.

11. 126 in.^{2}

12. Answers may vary slightly. $\approx$ 753.6 mm^2

■ Lesson 12.4

1. 216 cm^3 **2.** 90 in.^{3} **3.** 360 m^3

4. 4676 cm^3 **5.** 16 in.   **6.** 18 cm

7. 10 m

8. $V = 128$ in.^{3} **9.** $V = 108$ in.^{3}

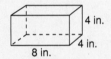   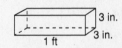

10. $V = 96$ in.^{3}

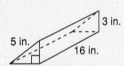

11. Each pillar requires 48 in.^{3}. All four require 192 in.^{3}.

■ Lesson 12.5

1. 50.24 m^3 **2.** 49,062.5 in.^{3}

3. 803.84 in.^{3} **4.** $\approx$ 3679.69 cm^3

5. 56.52 mm^3 **6.** 628 ft^3

7. 1017.36 in.^{3} **8.** 226.08 in.^{3} **9.** 22 in.

10. 7 cm   **11.** 19 mm   **12.** 2.5 ft

13. $r = 3.5$ in., $h = 2$ in., $V = 76.93$ in.^{3},
The radius of the cylinder is half of the width of the base of the prism. The height of the cylinder and prism are the same.
Extra space $= 119.07$ in.^{3}

14. Volume $= 4421.12$ in.^{3}
Time ≈ 36.8 minutes

■ Lesson 12.6

1. 128 cm^3 **2.** 160 in.^{3}

3. 201.0 m^3 **4.** 5887.5 cm^3

5. 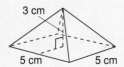 **6.**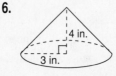

$V = 25$ cm^3 $V \approx 37.68$ in.^{3}

7. 682.7 cm^3 **8.** 962.9 cm^3 **9.** 24 in.^{3}

10. Yes, volume of cone ≈ 150.72 yd^3.

11. 6,250,000 tons

12. No, each cone requires ≈ 5.02 grams. For twelve the jeweler would need ≈ 60.24 grams.

■ Lesson 12.7

1. $4.5\pi \approx 14.1$ in.^{3}

2. $166.\overline{6}\pi \approx 523.3$ cm^3

3. $221.8\overline{3}\pi \approx 696.6$ in.^{3}

4. $3.658\overline{6}\pi \approx 11.5$ m^3

5. 2.61×10^{11}, 1.46×10^{10}, 2.23×10^{11}, 3.93×10^{10}, 3.65×10^{14}, 2.21×10^{14}, 1.75×10^{13}, 1.53×10^{13}, 1.51×10^9

6. 38.1 minutes

7. $\approx 385,173.3$ ft^3 **8.** $\approx 41,809.2$ cm^3

9. 20 mm, 20π mm, $1333.\overline{3}\pi$ mm^3 or $\frac{4000}{3}\pi$ mm^3

10. 18 in., 36 in., $17,496\pi$ in.^{3}

11. 5 yd, 10 yd, 10π yd

■ Lesson 12.8

1. Yes, 2:1 **2.** Yes, 2:3 **3.** Not similar

4. 256 in.^{2}, 224 in.^{3}

5. 2432π in.^{2}, 15360π in.^{3}

6. 324 cm^3, 1:3 **7.** 243 ft^2, 182.25 ft^3

8. 533.8 in.^{2}, 942.0 in.^{3}, 4804.2 in.^{2}, 25,434 in.^{3}

9. 108 in.^{2}, 72 in.^{3}, 675 in.^{2}, 1125 in.^{3}

10. 288 cm^2, 240 cm^3, 18 cm^2, 3.75 cm^3

11. 50 cm^3, 1350 cm^2

12. 113.04 in.^{3}, 7234.56 in.^{3}

13. 267.95 ft^3, 79.39 ft^3

■ Lesson 13.1

1. Yes **2.** No **3.** Yes

4. Answers vary.

x	−3	−2	−1	0	1	2	3
y	−7	−6	−5	−4	−3	−2	−1

5. Answers vary.

x	−8	−4	0	4	8
y	9	6	3	0	−3

6. Answers vary.

x	−6	−4	−2	0	2	4	6
y	8	7	6	5	4	3	2

7. Yes, for each 1 unit increase in x, there is a corresponding 4 unit increase in y.

8. Yes, for each 1 unit decrease in x, there is a corresponding 3 unit decrease in y.

9. $3x + \frac{1}{2}y = 10$,
Answers vary: (0, 20), (1, 14), (2, 8)

10. $x - 4y = -12$,
Answers vary: (−4, 2), (0, 3), (4, 4)

11. b, Answers vary: (80, 75), (100, 55), (90, 65)

12. c, Answers vary: (110, 70), (100, 80), (90, 90)

13. a, Answers vary: (70, 20), (10, 80), (30, 60)

14. 1920 **15.** 2340 **16.** 60 **17.** 2700

■ Lesson 13.2

1. b **2.** a **3.** c **4.** Yes **5.** Yes

6. No, Possible solution: (−4, −4) **7.** Yes

8. 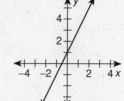 **9.**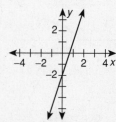

10.
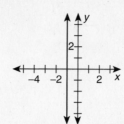

11.
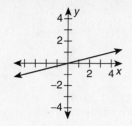

12.
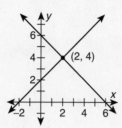

13.
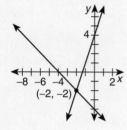

14. $c = 3$ **15.** $c = -6$

16.
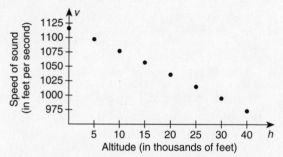

The points are close to being linear, but not exactly. The change in altitude in 5000 feet while the speed of sound drops 19 feet per second, then 20 feet per second, then 20, then 21, then 21, then 20 and lastly 22. The change is not exactly uniform, but very close.

■ Lesson 13.3

1. x-intercept: -3, y-intercept: 3

2. x-intercept: 2, y-intercept: -4

3. x-intercept: 2, y-intercept: 4

4.
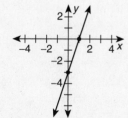

5.
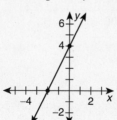

6.
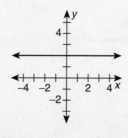

---

7. b   **8.** d   **9.** c   **10.** a

11. x-intercept: 1.98, y-intercept: 4.25

12. x-intercept: 2.81, y-intercept: -10.25

13. $(0, 32)$, $0°C$ is equivalent to $32°F$.
$(-17.\overline{7}, 0)$, $0°F$ is equivalent to $-17.\overline{7}°C$.

14. $(0, 16{,}500)$, After 0 years of ownership the car has value $16,500. $(11, 0)$, The car has $0 value after 11 years.

■ Lesson 13.4

1. Falls to the right   **2.** Rises to the right

3. Horizontal   **4.** $m = 4$ is steeper.

5. $m = -6$ is steeper.

6. $m = \frac{2}{5}$ **7.** $m = -\frac{5}{6}$ **8.** $m = -\frac{3}{5}$

9. $m = \frac{2}{5}$ **10.** $m = \frac{4}{3}$

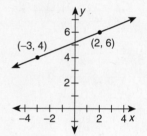

11. $m = 0$ **12.** $m = -\frac{5}{2}$

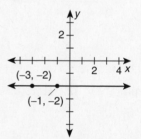   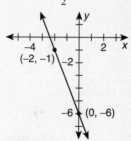

13. $m = \frac{1}{3}$ **14.** $m = \frac{14}{17}$ **15.** $m = \frac{8}{15}$

16. $m = -\frac{5}{12}$ **17.** $m = \frac{15}{8}$ **18.** $m = \frac{4}{3}$

19. $\overleftrightarrow{MN} \parallel \overleftrightarrow{XY}, m\overleftrightarrow{MN} = 3 = m\overleftrightarrow{XY}$

20. $\overleftrightarrow{MN} \not\parallel \overleftrightarrow{XY}, m\overleftrightarrow{MN} = \frac{1}{2}, m\overleftrightarrow{XY} = -\frac{1}{2}$

21. $\overleftrightarrow{MN} \not\parallel \overleftrightarrow{XY}, m\overleftrightarrow{MN} = 5, m\overleftrightarrow{XY} = \frac{1}{5}$

22. $\overleftrightarrow{MN} \parallel \overleftrightarrow{XY}, m\overleftrightarrow{MN} = \frac{2}{3} = m\overleftrightarrow{XY}$

■ Lesson 13.5

1. $m = 2$,
y-intercept: 4

2. $m = -\frac{1}{2}$,
y-intercept: 2

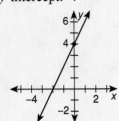

3. $m = 3$,
y-intercept: -2

4. $m = -4$,
y-intercept: 7

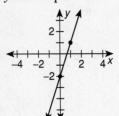

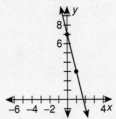

5. $m = -\frac{1}{10}$,
y-intercept: 0

6. $m = -2$,
y-intercept: 9

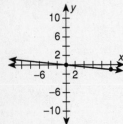

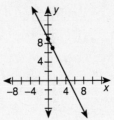

7. c   **8.** a   **9.** d   **10.** b

11. False, $m = \frac{1}{3}$; y-intercept: $-\frac{4}{3}$ **12.** True

13. False, $m = -\frac{3}{2}$, falls to right

14. True, $m = \frac{1}{3}$, rises to right and passes through origin.

15. $m = 1.68$; y-intercept: 31.88

16. 1.68 pounds   **17.** 58.76 pounds

18.

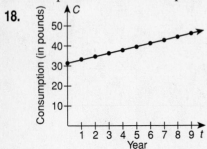

19. $y = \frac{1}{2}x + 2$ **20.** $y = 3x - 1$

21. $y = -3x - 3$

■ Lesson 13.6

1.

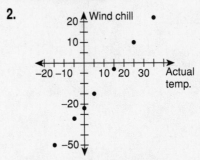

For 9 hours of practice the estimated score is approximately 70.

2.

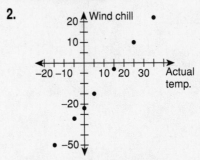

At a temperature of 20°F the wind chill factor is approximately 3°F. At a temperature of 10°F the wind chill factor is approximately −8°F.

3. a. Verbal model

$$\boxed{0.25} \times \boxed{\text{Number of quarters}} + \boxed{0.10}$$

$$\times \boxed{\text{Number of dimes}} = 50$$

Algebraic model

$0.25q + 0.10d = 50$

or

$25q + 10d = 5000$

b.

q	200	190	160	140	100
d	0	25	100	150	250

q	80	60	40	20	0
d	300	350	400	450	500

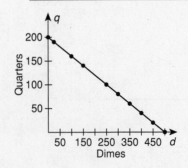

3. —CONTINUED—

  c. (0, 200)   0 dimes and 200 quarters totals $50.

    (500, 0)   500 dimes and 0 quarters totals $50.

4. a. $\boxed{0.03} \times \boxed{\text{Sales of sale priced goods}} + \boxed{0.04} \times$

$\boxed{\text{Sales of regular priced goods}} = \boxed{\$250 \text{ commission}}$

$0.03s + 0.04r = 250$

b.

s	0	1000	2000	3000	4000
r	6250	5500	4750	4000	3250

s	5000	6000	7000	8000	8333.3$\overline{3}$
r	2500	1750	1000	250	0

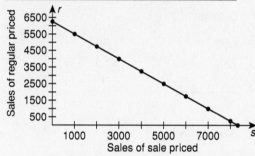

c. (0, 6250) $0 sales of sales priced goods + $6250 of sales of regular priced goods totals $250 commission.

(8333.33, 0) $8333.33 sales of sales priced goods + $0 of sales of regular priced goods totals $250 commission.

5. a. The times are decreasing almost linearly.

  b. The pattern is close to linear. If the pattern continues in 1996 the winning time could be approximately 48 seconds.

  c. Answers vary.

■ Lesson 13.7

1. Yes   **2.** No   **3.** No   **4.** Yes

5. Yes   **6.** Yes   **7.** b   **8.** c   **9.** a

10.

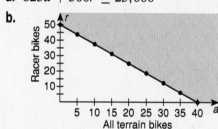

Possible solutions: (0, 4), (0, 5), (3, 6)

11.

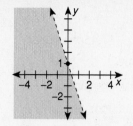

Possible solutions: $(-1, -1), (-2, 0),$ $(-3, -6)$

12.

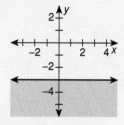

Possible solutions: $(0, -3), (1, -4), (2, -5)$

13. $b + 2g < 45$

14. $P \leq 400$ or $2l + 2w \leq 400$

15. $d - c \geq 42$ **16.** $j + p > 70$

17. a. $625a + 500r \geq 25,000$

  b.

c. Possible solutions: (0, 50), (10, 40), (20, 28), (30, 15), (40, 0)

18. $y < 2x + 1$ **19.** $y \geq -x$

20. $y < -2x - 2$

■ Lesson 13.8

1. Estimates vary, $\sqrt{72} \approx 8.49$

2. Estimates vary, $\sqrt{80} \approx 8.94$

3. Estimates vary, $\sqrt{73} \approx 8.54$

4. Estimates vary, $\left(\frac{7}{2}, \frac{1}{2}\right)$

5. Estimates vary, $\left(-\frac{5}{2}, 0\right)$

6. Estimates vary, $\left(-\frac{1}{2}, -\frac{1}{2}\right)$

7. Center at (0, 0), radius ≈ 4.1

8. $WY = XZ = \sqrt{40} \approx 6.32$

9. b.

■ Lesson 14.1

1. 31, 30.5, 30   **2.** 17.6, 17.45, no mode

3. 9, 9, 8   **4.** 47, 48, 48   **5.** 20

6. 12.8, 14, 14   **7.** Answers vary.

8.–10. Measures and explanations vary.

11. 5   **12.** $\approx$ 2.8, 3, 3

13. Possible answer: The mode would be the best measure because the comparison was one of quantity.

14. 71,000; 65,500; 96,000

15. Possible answer: The median because the very high priced homes distorts the mean.

■ Lesson 14.2

1. 30, 42, 43, 52, 53, 53, 54, 61, 67, 67, 68, 70, 71, 72, 72, 73

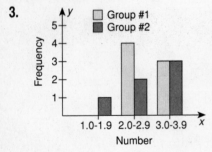

2. Group #1: 2.6, 2.7, 2.8, 2.9, 3.3, 3.5, 3.5

Group #2: 1.9, 2.0, 2.1, 3.8, 3.8, 3.9

3.

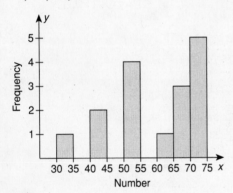

4.

```
6 | 0 0 2
5 | 0 1 1 1 3 3
4 | 1 2 3 7 7 9
3 | 0 2 3 3 3 4 5 6 6 7 9 9 9
2 | 0 0 3 3 4 4 5 5 6 7 8 8 9
1 | 2 3 6 6 7 7 8 9 9
```

6|0 represents 60.

5.

```
0.39 | 0
0.38 | 8
0.37 |
0.36 | 1 3 3 4 6 8
0.35 | 0 7 9
0.34 | 1 3 3
0.33 | 2 3 3 6 7 9
0.32 | 9 9
0.31 | 8
```

6.

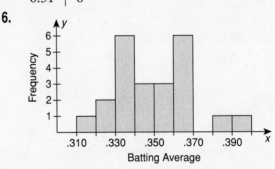

Batting Average

■ Lesson 14.3

1. 1 and 40   **2.** 7, 18, and 29

3. 75%   **4.** 25%   **5.** 50%

6.

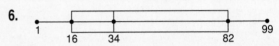

7. Answers vary.

8.

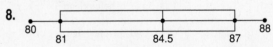

9.

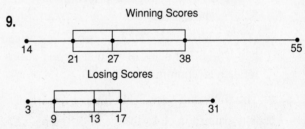

10. Answers vary.

11. Data can vary. Possible real-life situations: exam scores with extra credit, golf scores, or basketball scores.

■ Lesson 14.4

1. $\begin{bmatrix} 0 & 5 \\ 9 & -3 \end{bmatrix}$, $\begin{bmatrix} 6 & -9 \\ -1 & 3 \end{bmatrix}$

2. $\begin{bmatrix} 5 & 9 \\ 6 & 1 \end{bmatrix}$, $\begin{bmatrix} 15 & 5 \\ -12 & 3 \end{bmatrix}$

3. $\begin{bmatrix} 1 & 2 & 0 \\ 17 & -3 & 11 \end{bmatrix}$, $\begin{bmatrix} 5 & 2 & -10 \\ -3 & 3 & 7 \end{bmatrix}$

4. $\begin{bmatrix} 15 & -6 \\ 3 & 8 \\ 2 & -5 \end{bmatrix}$, $\begin{bmatrix} -3 & 10 \\ -9 & 0 \\ 8 & -9 \end{bmatrix}$

5. $a = \frac{3}{2}$, $b = 6$, $c = 3$, $d = 4$

6. Many correct answers.

7. Many correct answers.

8. $\begin{bmatrix} 635 & 758 \\ 785 & 823 \\ 814 & 730 \end{bmatrix}$, $\begin{bmatrix} 215 & 295 \\ 293 & 320 \\ 345 & 292 \end{bmatrix}$

9. Stand 1 - August
   Stand 2 - July

10. $\begin{bmatrix} 420 & 463 \\ 492 & 503 \\ 470 & 438 \end{bmatrix}$

11. Stand 2 - $1404 profit

■ Lesson 14.5

1. Yes, a trinomial   **2.** Yes, a binomial

3. Not a polynomial

4. b, $2x^2 + 9x + 6$ **5.** c, $2x^2 + 12x + 8$

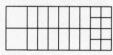

6. a, $4x^2 + 6x + 8$

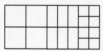

7. $-2z^3 + 14z^2 + 3z$, $-2z^3$, $14z^2$, $3z$

8. $6x^4 + \frac{1}{2}x^2 - 2x$, $6x^4$, $\frac{1}{2}x^2$, $-2x$

9. $-3y^3 - 2y + 10$, $-3y^3$, $-2y$, 10

10. $-2x^2 + 10x$ **11.** $z^4 - 7z^2 + z$

12. $-15x^2 + 11$ **13.** $\frac{19}{5}m^2 - 17$

14.

t	1	2	3	4	5
h	1438	1390	1310	1198	1054

t	6	7	8	9	10
h	878	670	430	158	-146

15. 878 ft   **16.** Between 9 and 10 seconds

17. 54 ft, -262 ft; It takes between 10 and 11 seconds for the penny to strike the ground.

■ Lesson 14.6

1.
$$\begin{array}{r} -4x^3 + 2x^2 \qquad\quad - 4 \\ + -3x^3 \qquad\quad + 2x + 8 \\ \hline -7x^3 + 2x^2 + 2x + 4 \end{array}$$

2.
$$\begin{array}{r} 3x^3 + 2x^2 - 6x + 7 \\ - (2x^3 - 6x^2 - 4x - 8) \\ \hline x^3 + 8x^2 - 2x + 15 \end{array}$$

3. $5x^2 + x - 10$ **4.** $-k^3 - 3k^2 + 2k + 12$

5. $4w^3 - w^2 - 2w - 18$

6. $-2d^4 - d^3 - 9d^2 - 6d - 18$

7. $6x^3 - 13x^2 + 12x - 5$

8. $3y^4 - 17y^3 - 13y^2 + 12y - 21$

9. $-16x + 23$ **10.** $-9k^2 - 14k + 18$

11. $w^2 + 11w - 8$ **12.** $x^3 + x^2 + 4x - 9$

13. $3x^2 + 9x - 34$, 230   **14.** $x^2 + 7x + 4$, 124

15. $7x^2 + 11x$, 96   **16.** $-3x^2 + 36x + 80$, 161

■ Lesson 14.7

1. $12x^3 - 6x$ **2.** $-3t^5 - 2t^3 + 3t^2$

3. $6w^5 - 18w^3 - 6w$ **4.** $-12c^4 + 24c^2$

5. $-6x^4 + 6x^3 - 12x^2 + 15x$

6. $-n^7 + 3n^6 - 2n^5 + 6n^3$

7. $7z^3 - 3z^2 + 2z$ **8.** $-18k^4 + 12k^2 + 42k$

9. $3p^4 - 2p^3 + 6p^2$

10. I: $4x^2 + 3x$, II: $10x^2 - 20x$, III: $4x^2 + 3x$

11. $18x^2 - 14x$

12. $\frac{1}{2}(2x)[(5x - 10) + (13x - 4)] = 18x^2 - 14x$

13. They are equivalent.

14. $n(n - 3) = n^2 - 3n$

15. $x^2(2x + 5) = 2x^3 + 5x^2$

16. $\frac{1}{2}(5x)(6x + 2) = 15x^2 + 5x$

17. $150x^3 + 50x^2$ **18.** $220x^2 + 40x$

19. $V = 4500$ cm³; $SA = 2100$ cm²

■ Lesson 14.8

1. $(3x + 5)(2x + 4) = (3x + 5)(2x) + (3x + 5)(4)$
$$= 6x^2 + 10x + 12x + 20$$
$$= 6x^2 + 22x + 20$$

2. $5x^2 + 11x + 2$ **3.** $3x^2 + 19x + 20$

4. $2x^2 + 15x + 28$ **5.** $12x^2 + 30x + 12$

6. $2x^2 + 17x + 36$ **7.** $15x^2 + 19x + 6$

8. $12x^2 + 60x + 72$ **9.** $20x^2 + 91x + 99$

10. $42x^2 + 142x + 120$ **11.** $x^2 + \frac{15}{2}x + 9$

12. $5x^2 + \frac{35}{2}x + 15$ **13.** $6x^2 + 11x + 4$

14. $x^2 + 14x + 30$ **15.** $8x + 18$

16. $(4x + 2)$ by $(3x + 2)$
   Area $= 12x^2 + 14x + 4$

17. $(4x + 5)$ by $(3x + 4)$
   Area $= 12x^2 + 31x + 20$